Praise for

Said the Lady with the Blue Hair

"A refreshing, heart warming read that has lessons for direct selling beginners as well as experienced leaders at all levels. Also recommend for corporate executives in parent organizations, as alignment with a company's values is a cornerstone of any direct seller's success. As Kai learns and practices Belle's 7 Rules for Success, she transforms from neophyte to a mentor/coach, understanding the integration of her 'why' and her life/work balance."

~**Angie Rossi**, Avon Group Vice President - North America Sales – Retired

"A simply terrific book that combines an immensely engaging story you won't be able to put down along with the powerful principles needed to build a successful Direct Selling business. Follow 'Belle's' Rules' and you'll find yourself serving many more people, earning a significantly higher income, and most important of all, living a life of joy and happiness. If you're a Direct Sales Leader…you'll want to promote this book to your entire team, both established veterans and those who've just joined! It's that impactful!"

~**Bob Burg,** coauthor of *The Go-Giver* and Go-Giver Book Series

"I enjoyed reading *Said the Lady With the Blue Hair*. Knowing Lisa Wilber, coauthor - direct seller extraordinaire, the parable reads a bit like an autobiography. There are many subtleties for the reader. Principles and values are vividly described and emphasized. This parable is actually a tribute to all direct sellers who have built their businesses focused on the products and services they love, the customers and team members they serve. This is a story about how ordinary can become extraordinary!"

~**John T. Fleming,** Principal Ideas & Design Group, LLC, Author - Ultimate Gig, The One Course, LEVERAGE

"A delightful story filled with wit and wisdom that will have you laughing and tearing up—and sometimes at the same time! The characters felt like dear friends and I did not want the story to end. The book masterfully shares Belle's "7 Rules for Success in Direct Sales." It raises the standard for the direct sales profession. If you are just starting in direct sales or you're a successful leader, you will want to read this little gem and pass it along to as many people in your organization as possible."

~**Kathy Tagenel**, President, Go-Givers International

"Are you starting a direct sales business? Need some guard rails to stay on track? It is easy to follow every tip we hear, but we forget to have a strategy for success. Belle's 7 rules help direct sellers create their business by serving others. Follow Kai's development story as she discovers her way to becoming a direct sales team builder."

~**Tom "Big Al" Schreiter**, author of the Big Al books network marketing series.
www.BigAlBooks.com

"*Said the Lady with the Blue Hair* starts with a poignant question: Who knew? The protagonist of this short novella is Kai, an unexpectedly single mother who has just been widowed. She must create a new life in circumstances she never anticipated, and she feels very much alone. That challenge is familiar to all too many people: Nobody ever knows what the future will bring. This business parable walks the reader through the inspiring story of how Kai builds a new life by creating an independent career for herself. The book's subtitle may be specific - *7 Rules for Success in Direct Sales Wrapped in a Wonderful Lesson for Life* — but its user-friendly advice offers encouragement and guidance for anyone facing the need to reinvent themselves."

~**Leslie Bennetts,** Author of *The Feminine Mistake* and *Last Girl Before Freeway,* Longtime Writer for *Vanity Fair,* Former Reporter for *The New York Times,* Speaker on Women's Empowerment and Financial Security

Issues. Published in, *Thirty Ways of Looking at Hillary, The Secret Currency of Love* and other anthologies.

"This book will grab you the minute you start reading. While it is jam-packed with sage advice for direct sales, it also shares a heart-felt story about a widow's struggle to build a life and financial security for her daughter and her. I have tried my hand at direct sales over the years and I never had much success. How I wish I'd had this book to guide me along the way. For those of you who think you might not be good at direct sales, this is a must read. You'll close the book and quickly dive into a world of success and excitement. For those of you already involved in direct sales, this book with help you soar to the next level of success. Thanks to my friends Jeff and Lisa for writing such an outstanding, helpful, book.

~Susan Solovic – THE Small Business Expert, Regular Contributor to Fox Business News, New York Times, Wall Street Journal, USA Today and Amazon Bestselling Author of *It's Your Biz: The Complete Guide to Becoming Your Own Boss* and *The Girl's Guide to Building a Million Dollar Business*.

"I've been in the Direct Sales/Network Marketing industry for decades. I am the founder of TheNetworkMarketingMagazine.com for going on 18 years. I've been responsible for reading thousands of articles written by the Best of the Best. Lisa Wilber and Jeff West have given us one of the best gifts in their latest books, *Said the Lady with the Blue Hair.* This is a wonderfully engaging story that all of us will embrace. It has lessons we can put into action in our own business, right away. Make sure that you not only get a copy of this future bestseller, but encourage your entire team to embrace this wonderful book for themselves."

~George Madiou, Founder and Publisher of https:// TheNetworkMarketingMagazine.com

"Being in direct sales for almost 20 years, I have experienced everything in this book from the person looking for something in their life to the person who grows into the one who wants to help others. Every person who wants to know where direct sales can lead them or how to be a leader with heart should read *Said the Lady with Blue Hair*. Entertaining, Relatable, and Honest to a T! Can't wait to get this in the hands of my team and share it with my tribe!"

~Molly Stone-Bibb, Bronze Executive Leader, National Recruiter & Trainer at New Avon, LLC

"What a great story about perseverance and finding your path in life! *Said the Lady with the Blue Hair* had my attention from the beginning! Kai's character is very relatable for many people encountering direct sales for the first time. The quirky humor and Kai's enthusiasm to learn made this a fun read! The lessons in business and practical advice make this book a great read for anyone new in the industry. It is also a valuable guide for any leaders building a team. The 7 Rules for Success in Direct Sales can be followed in any organization you choose to join."

~Barb Miller, Super Affiliate with My Daily Choice, Mega Million Club Inner Circle

"Tell me what to do and I can promise I'll soon lose interest. That's why I don't finish 9 out of 10 'How To' books I start. But tell me a story. Hook me with real, interesting people I fall in like with… in love with. People whose lives I don't just read about, but *experience*… then you've got me. The *Said the Lady with the Blue Hair* story got me… good. Then it ever-so cleverly taught me things. Some I knew. Some I didn't. The best ones were things I *thought I knew,* but was shown in such a way that I got them more and better than ever before."

~John Milton Fogg, Author of the million-selling book, *The Greatest Networker in the World*

"I enjoyed success by accidentally obeying some of the rules Lisa and Jeff explain in, *Said the Lady with Blue Hair*. You don't have to wait for an accident. Just read this book."

~**Dan Rockwell,** *Inc Magazine* Top 50 Leadership Expert and author of *Leadership Freak*

"This story connects! It connects you to who you are and what you value most. It connects you to the impact you can have in the world - with others. It connects you to the disciplines of success. You'll connect with the characters too. They will move your heart and inspire action. This story is for anyone who is designing a life around what they love. It is filled with wisdom and beautifully human."

~**Dondi Scumaci**, Author of *Designed for Success: Ten Commandments for Women in the Workplace*, and *Ready, Set…Grow and Career Moves*.

"The Lady With the Blue Hair" and I have known each other for over 25 years! I can honestly say that her 7 Rules have been the basis for my very successful career in Direct Sales. But don't be fooled. These "Rules" have become the Guide Stones for a successful life. Taking these rules and applying them to every area of life has proved successful. In the direct sales world, the non-profit management world, and even in our home life. Indeed, if you're not applying these simple rules, you're just not trying hard enough!

~**Deby Sorensen,** Lifetime Member DSWA, 2SunsetSailors on: Facebook/Instagram/YouTube

"Such a fun read with truly valuable insight on building a successful Direct Selling business and just as importantly, a wonderful life! 'Belle's Rules' are like having a step-by-step guide to greatness!"

~**April Shprintz,** Creator of The Generosity Culture® & Author of Magic Blue Rocks, The Secret to Doing Anything.

"Selling stuff can seem hard—almost a daunting task, especially if you don't place yourself in the right framework of critical mindsets and philosophies going into the game. With this wonderfully told story, Lisa and Jeff take their reader down a well-lit path that will help them begin to create the framework (rules) needed for a successful career in sales. It sometimes takes a salesperson a LIFETIME to identify these seven "rules." The authors have given you the ability to learn them inside of a three or four hour read!"

~**Joe Buzzello**, Creator - The CAP Equation Sales Methodology, Co-Founder - growth10 and mentumm

"I was hooked to this incredible story from the moment I started reading *Said the Lady with Blue Hair.* Whether you are brand new in sales or have been in business for years there are so many incredible takeaways and best practices shared around Sales, Leadership, and making a difference to those around you. I love reading books where I can apply insightful tips right away to help take my business to the next level. I would highly recommend this book to anyone who wants to get better personally and professionally."

~**Aspen Madrid,** Aflac Market Director for Iowa/Minnesota

"Wow! Wow! Wow! Did I say wow! This has been such a captivating weekend read. A very thorough recapitulation of the necessary principles to networking and direct sales success, laid out in very relatable situations. The 7 Rules that Belle shares in *Said the Lady with the Blue Hair* truly lay the groundwork not just for business success but also can be applied in other areas of life. I cannot wait my second read."

~**Suronna Nortan,** Account Executive, The Avon Company

"Kai had my heart from go…. And that's what direct sales is all about….. the heart to heart connections between REAL people…. With REAL fears, hopes and desires to make a difference. Bravo to Lisa and Jeff!! What a wonder-full read!"

"Selling isn't just about closing, it's truly about connecting. And this story connects!!! Emphasizing that our greatest influence is in our impact and value we provide to others, this gem of a story shares with us how to do this as our authentic self, through characters in the book that emulate what we go through and grow through best in life. If you want to "build a life you don't need a vacation from and a business customers are drawn too" this is a fantastic book to put you on that path."

~Dennis Giannetti, National Sales Speaker and Trainer, Mastermind Leader, VIP Retreat and Results Coach.

" Although this story may have a focus towards direct sales, I think that is a bit unfair. In my business, and with the many clients I serve, I can't think of any where the "7 Rules of Success" would not be extremely beneficial to them and for life in general. It demonstrates vividly how adverse events can be turned into positive life changing circumstances. Add to that a great story and you have a winner"

~Fred Dannhauser, Area President, Focus CFO

"A special little story about a very special person helping another very special person. Whether you find yourself in the mentor or mentee roles... or someone who could be either of those, this book is for you. The 7 rules are time-tested and absolutely work without a shadow of a doubt. You will enjoy these lessons wrapped in a wonderful story that is easy and quick to read. Enjoy and learn. What a great combination!"

~Donna Stott, Broker and Coach, Northwest Atlanta Properties & Property Management and Your Coaching Matters

"Who knew that reading a book about success tips in direct sales could make me cry, laugh, giggle, snort, and relate to the characters so deeply that I already have appointments on my calendar to implement some of the rules in my own life and business? This book is a must-read for anyone asking themselves, "How do I get unstuck in my business or life?"

~**Shell Vera,** Marketer, Voice Discovery Coach, Writer

"This is absolutely the best book I have ever read about how to succeed in direct sales. It is also a roadmap for a happy fulfilled life! It is told in an engaging beautiful story that will hold your interest and make you smile and even laugh here and there. The 7 Rules for Success are right on and will help you live your best live whether in direct sales or not."

~**Pat Puzder,** Inner Circle Executive Leader, Avon 2012 Woman of Enterprise, National Spirit of Albee 12 Consecutive Years

"Jeff and Lisa have done a brilliant job of weaving together interesting characters, entertaining stories, and a series of business and life principles that can help anyone looking to have a success business that makes an impact in the lives of others. Bravo!"

~**Christie Ruffino**, Master Story Activator

"*Said The Lady With The Blue Hair* is not just another self help book about being a better salesperson. This book is entertaining, engaging, funny, and heartfelt. The 7 rules are presented in a unique way and can also be applied to life in general. The story helps us change the way we think about people, our careers, and building relationships. If you are in sales, this is a great book that you will certainly learn from. If you are someone who would like to learn about building relationships or changing your quality of life, this book will work for you too. Great job Lisa and Jeff."

~**Mitch H. Bailey**, President, MB5 Financial Group

"A BLUE-HAIRED LADY LIKE NO OTHER! Shattering the stereotype of blue-haired ladies is just the beginning of the fun and new perspectives you'll discover in *Said the Lady with the Blue Hair*. This book combines powerful life-lessons along with proven direct-selling insights… all wrapped in a warm, entertaining, and relatable parable. Lisa and Jeff team up to create a story featuring three distinct themes - at least one of which you're certain to relate with … and a high likelihood you'll achieve the trifecta and gain value from all three. Where you're simply interested in a read filled with warmth, are seeking to adapt to a new direction of your life, or are striving to create a profitable success journey via direct sales - this book is a must read."

~Bill Ellis, Brand Architect, Branding for Results

"What a fun read, and so relatable. From the characters to the personal feelings and experiences. You'll catch yourself nodding your head and smiling as you read this book. Besides Belle's 7 Rules for success, you will also find so many easy-to-follow tips sprinkled throughout the story that will help you in your direct sales business. I can't wait to share this with my team! Everyone needs a "Belle" in their life!"

~Theresa Paul, Goddess, Avon Silver Executive Leader

"What an amazing read! This story puts direct sales in a new perspective. Jeff and Lisa give us into the life of a salesperson and how sales can be fun for both them and the customer. This book is written in a way that allows the reader to feel joy, to cry, and to learn along with the characters. They remind us that each one of us is worthy, and that we can and should create a path to our dreams."

~ Robert and Noelle Peterson, The Smiling Coaching Couple

"If you're considering a career in direct sales, you need to start by reading *Said the Lady with the Blue Hair* first. It's an enjoyable read that takes you on the journey of Kai, a young widow who's trying to rebuild her life with her daughter. She finds her inspiration in a chance meeting with a blue-haired lady named Belle on the beach in Hawaii. Written in parable form, you are introduced to Belle's 7 Rules for creating a direct sales business while serving others. This book is an excellent "blueprint" for women who want to build an extraordinary business with integrity that fits into their life and their goals. The advice provided in the book is spot on, which is not a surprise since co-author Lisa Wilber is a direct seller extraordinaire/mentor and is the embodiment of Belle in real life. It's such a refreshing change from other books on sales. Grab a copy and start reading."

~ **Linda Locke**, Writer, Business Coach

Also by the Authors

Authored and Co-authored by Lisa M. Wilber

Marketing Ideas for the Wild at Heart: copyright © (1997)

Support, Support, Support: the Three Most Important Things about Network Marketing:

copyright © (1999)

Over the Edge: More Marketing Ideas for the Wild at Heart: copyright © (2002)

Build It Big: 101 Insider Secrets from Top Direct Selling Experts: copyright © (2005)

More Build It Big: 101 Insider Secrets from Top Direct Selling Experts: copyright © (2006)

Getting Things Done: Successful Women Speak: copyright © (2006)

It's Time for Network Marketing: the Most Remarkable Form of Free Enterprise Ever Created: copyright © (2007)

A View from the Top: Avon's Elite Leaders Share Their Stories and Strategies to Succeed:

copyright © (2012)

A View from the Top Volume 2: Avon's Elite Leaders Share Their Stories and Strategies to Succeed: copyright © (2013)

A View from the Top Volume 3: Avon's Elite Leaders Share Their Stories and Strategies to Succeed: copyright © (2015)

Success Chronicles: Network Marketing Women of Impact: copyright © (2018)

by Jeff C. West

The Unexpected Tour Guide: copyright © 2013

Fusion Points® Engage the Science of Persistence: copyright© 2015

The 7.5 Essential Selling Skills: copyright © 2016

Survival Skills for Commission Salespeople in Insurance: copyright© 2018

Said the Lady with the Blue Hair

7 Rules for Success in Direct Sales
Wrapped in a Wonderful Lesson for Life

Said the Lady with the Blue Hair

7 Rules for Success in Direct Sales Wrapped in a Wonderful Lesson for Life

by

Lisa M. Wilber and Jeff C. West

Published by

West Marketing Group, INC

PO Box 752

Giddings, TX 78942

www.jeffcwest.com

Library of Congress Control Number: 2022917215

ISBN: 978-0-9973614-3-8 (Paperback)

ISDN: ISBN: 978-0-9973614-6-9 (Hardback)

eISBN: 978-0-9973614-4-5 (eReader)

Editing by Jessi Akins

Book cover design by Alexx M. Wilber.

Love Notes

From Lisa…

With dozens and dozens of people who have offered their assistance with this and other projects, for which I am extremely grateful, my hope is that you will allow me to dedicate this paragraph in this book to my son (and cover artist) Alexx Wilber. Never did I dream that, when I adopted you as an infant in 2005, you would bring such depth and fullness to my life. From the many travels we have gone on together, to watching you play soccer and perform in musicals - you have brought so many new experiences to my world - and continue to do so. Your ability to "lean in" to the crazy Mom experience which I am is appreciated. My world turns because of you. Thank you for being my kid.

From Jeff…

Thank you Bob Burg and Kathy Tagenel for your friendship, mentorship and building a community of Go-Givers who touch my heart in such a meaningful way. Thank you Ana Gabriel Mann and John David Mann for being such sweet souls… John, you are the greatest storyteller of our time. And thank you to my daughters Lindsay and Whitney. You make me want to be a better person everyday… love you to the moon and back… and then some.

$$\boxed{\textbf{1}}$$

Who knew?

The sun was rising and warming Kai's back while the cool mist from a small cloud directly above drifted down upon her like the dandelions she blew into the air as a child. When paired with the ocean breeze moving slowly across Poipu Beach, the combination gave her a slight chill. She pulled her red-and-black kimono from her beach bag, draped it across her legs, and took another sip of coffee from her travel mug.

Who knew? she thought to herself again.

Who knew last December that she would be sitting here again, exactly a year later, on their favorite beach in Kauai watching the green sea turtles as they nested in the early morning?

Alone.

I'm not supposed to be here alone! We planned this trip together. We come to Kauai every year in December. That is the way it has always been and that's the way it is supposed to be now!

Well, she wasn't really alone. Her ten-year-old daughter, Michaela, was lying beside her curled up in a couple of beach towels… sleeping.

Kai smiled as she looked at her daughter. She was so beautiful and perfect as she napped.

Ahh. She is a perfect angel… when she sleeps!

Kai laughed quietly as her thoughts danced back and forth through the slideshow of images that made up Michaela's life. In her mind's eye, Kai always saw Michaela at every age she had ever been. Curled up in those towels, she saw the seven-pound four-ounce infant with the most beautiful dark hair curled on top of her head. She saw the toddler, stumbling as she took her first steps. She saw the excited and frightened little girl going to her first day of kindergarten dressed in the cutest outfit of red pants, a white shirt and a matching red vest.

And yes, now there was this delicate, and at times overly insistent, little ten year old who was always a perfect angel… when she slept.

Kai's laughter caused Michaela to stir slightly.

"What are you laughing at, Mom?"

"Oh. Nothing."

"Yes, you were. I wasn't asleep, Mom. I heard you," she said, yawning and stretching as she sat up.

She moved closer, sliding underneath Kai's arm.

Kai hugged her daughter, gave her a kiss on the head and said, "I was just thinking about you."

"And I made you laugh?"

"I was just remembering you and how wonderful it's been watching you grow up. I am so glad that I get to be your mother. I can't wait to watch you as you become a woman and maybe have a little girl of your own someday."

Michaela put her arms around her mother and held her tightly.

"Promise?"

"Promise what?"

"Promise that you'll watch me grow up? Promise that you'll never go away?"

Hearing those words took Kai's breath for a second.

She pulled Michaela a little closer, rested her chin on top of her head, and turned her face toward the area on the beach that was roped off in yellow tape… warning where the sea turtles were laying their eggs in the sand.

She didn't want Michaela to see her eyes as they welled up with tears… again.

"I promise, baby."

"Dad didn't keep that promise. Do you promise you will?"

"It wasn't that dad didn't keep that promise, Michaela. He couldn't keep that promise. If there was any way that he could have… he would've."

"How do you know you'll keep it?"

Kai took a slow deep breath, closed her eyes for a few seconds and thought about her answer. It was a perfectly understandable question from a ten-year-old girl who had experienced the unexpected death of her father. A question for which Kai wasn't sure she had an answer.

Michael, Kai's husband and Michaela's namesake, had been a specimen of good health. He ate a healthy diet, exercised regularly, and really took great care of himself. As a child, he had often been

3

sick with allergies and asthma. So as an adult, he went to the extra effort to try and avoid repeating some of those same health issues.

He had also built a successful company which he had actually started in college not long before he and Kai first met.

He was a great father to Michaela. He was a great husband to Kai.

Everything was perfect.

Until it wasn't.

Michael came in one evening after work, complaining about a cough that he just couldn't seem to shake.

"My allergies have been getting the best of me over the last few days," he told Kai. "I think I'll run by the doctor's office tomorrow and see if I can get one of those steroid shots or a prescription. I'd like to get ahead of this thing."

He was feeling worse when he woke the next morning. So after dropping Michaela off at school, Kai drove Michael to the clinic.

The next few days were somewhat of a blur in Kai's mind.

Michael went straight from the doctor's office to the hospital. He was admitted immediately.

Two days later, he was put into ICU.

Two days after that, he was gone.

Who knew?

Kai was alone.

She was scared.

Even though Michael had made all of the necessary financial arrangements to ensure that Kai and Michaela wouldn't end up on the street, Kai was keenly aware that she had to learn things now that she'd never needed to know before.

She remembered telling her best friend, Lindsay, "I know this sounds crazy, but I don't even know how to 'adult' in many ways. Michael always balanced the bank accounts and paid the bills. He made enough money that I could devote my time to Michaela and our home.

"I am great at running a house. I am great at running the schedules of my family. But I have now got to learn how to do so much more. And I have to learn to balance them all. I also have to build a career now, and I am not so sure that my degree in ancient European history is going to prove to be all that helpful on the job market."

She had laughed a little as she held back her tears and told Lindsay, "Thank God I minored in obscure antiquities from western China, otherwise I don't know what I would do!"

Kai was certainly going through some difficult times. But, now, holding Michaela ever so tightly — she was again reminded that, though her personal struggles were quite real, here in her arms was an amazing little girl who was scared about the future and needed her mother more than ever before.

"Michaela, the truth about life is that I don't know that for sure. But most people do live a nice long life. Most people don't leave us so early. I think the average life expectancy is somewhere around eighty-years now. So you and I should be a team for many years to come."

Michaela didn't say anything. She just kept holding her mother tightly.

Kai said, "Why don't you tell me your favorite story about your dad? I have my own. But I would really like to hear yours."

Michaela thought for a few seconds, remembering her dad. They were quite close, and there were so many things about him that she held dearly in her heart. At one point, she actually complained that it

5

was "kinda weird" that a daughter could be named after her father. But now, she was so very glad that she was. It was like keeping a little piece of her dad with her.

"I love how he made me laugh so much."

"What do you mean?"

"I don't know. He would say silly things that I didn't get at first. But once I understood them, I would laugh."

"Like what?"

"Well, when anyone would ask him how he was doing, he would always give them silly answers. Like if someone asked: 'How are you today, Michael?' Dad would answer, 'If I were doing any better, I'd be twins. And that would make my wife, Kai, a very unhappy woman. One of me is enough!'"

The mother and daughter both began to laugh.

Michaela quickly thought of another example: "Or he'd say something like" (lowering her voice and doing her best impression of her dad) "'Well, I feel a whole lot more like I do right now than I did the other day.'

"Or when he would walk into someplace and say, 'I've lost my mind. Have you seen it in here? It's quite small and I don't want anyone to step on it.'"

Their laughter grew.

Kai said, "My favorite was when your dad would greet checkers at the grocery store. As soon as they looked at him, but before they could say anything, he would say, 'Hi! How am I doing?'

"Most of the time they would just look at him with that, "I didn't study for this exam" look on their faces. But a particularly sharp young lady once said, 'You're doing fine! How am I?'

"Your dad cracked up and said, 'You win! That's the best response I've had yet!'"

As their laughter began to die down a bit, Kai looked at Michaela, gave her a comforting smile and said, "I'm not sure how everything is going to work out, baby. But I promise you that it will. And we will handle it together."

Michaela hugged Kai a little tighter.

On the beach in front of them, Kai noticed a couple of perfectly formed cone shells — white with transparent streaks of orange—with brown specks that made perfect spirals from top to bottom.

"Oh!" said Kai. "Those cone shells were your dad's favorites. Would you like to grab a couple and put them in your keepsake box with things of your father's?"

Michaela thought for a minute.

"I think I'll take a picture of them and put that in the box instead. I remember dad being pretty protective of the beaches here. I think that's what he'd want me to do."

"You're probably right," replied Kai as she smiled.

She gave her daughter another hug and a soft kiss.

"He would be so very proud of you."

Who knew? she thought again.

Who knew?

2

The day had traveled into mid-morning, and the beach was becoming much more active.

Sunbathers were staking out their places along the beach, neatly arranging their towels and chairs, and pulling out their hats, sunglasses and tubes of various lotions. Some were already applying sunscreen to themselves and their children. Music of various types began to fill the air. Not so loud as to be a bother. More like a blended musical universe of twinkling melodies instead of stars.

Late-arriving surfers, both novice and expert, or as Kai had come to know them over the years, "kooks" and "shreds," were paddling their boards out into the ocean, planning on catching their first waves of the day. Kai could always tell the experience level by how relaxed they were as they mounted their longboards.

The kooks would usually look like sumo wrestlers as they got onto their feet and squatted on their boards in what the locals referred to as their "poop stance." Kai laughed to herself as she imagined seeing one of them actually doing the sumo wrestler stomp and falling into the water!

She remembered Michael once saying, "Well, I'd much rather see them do that sumo-wrestler stomp than anything remotely matching the term *poop stance*!" To which Michaela and Kai both yelled, "EEEEWW!"

The shreds, on the other hand, were the accomplished surfers. They would paddle out and wait in the line up, joking back and forth until their choice of wave would come in. If it was a really great wave, a few surfers would ride at the same time. This "party wave" was fun to watch.

Kai and Michael had met an older lady last year who was an outstanding surfer. She was in great shape, very tan, and had wrinkle lines around her mouth that perfectly matched her delightful smile.

The lady had encouraged Kai to join her on the waves. She even offered to give her a couple of lessons and provide the longboard. Kai accepted her kind offer and the two of them had a great time.

Kai laughed as she remembered teasing Michael.

He had heard someone call the lady "Betty," so naturally he did so as well.

"Betty, you are A-Mazing out there!"

"Betty, do you think you can teach me after you teach Kai?'

"Betty, where are you from?"

It wasn't until several days later that Kai informed him that "Betty" was not her name. It was a term used for a lady surfer who was quite old. And since "Betty" was only in her sixties, the term didn't really fit.

Michael was so embarrassed! He had to apologize to the lady as soon as he saw her. "Betty" and Kai both thought it was hilarious!

I wonder if I will see "Betty" again this year? Kai thought as she began to arrange their breakfast.

Kai pulled out a granola bar and a bottle of juice from her beach bag. She unwrapped the bar, opened the juice and handed both to Michaela. She chose a mango for herself and continued to sip her coffee.

"This is a great place to have breakfast, isn't it?" said Kai, totally oblivious to a particularly well-built young man who was walking in front of them. "The view is incredible!"

Michaela, on the other hand, had noticed the young man.

"GROSS, Mom!"

"What?"

Michaela giggled a little, and pointed toward the man.

Kai lowered her sunglasses to the tip of her nose, and for a couple of seconds, she studied the form of the man who was indeed quite handsome and muscular.

She pushed her sunglasses back into position, raised an eyebrow and said, "Hmm. I was actually talking about the ocean. But now that you mention it…"

"Again, GROSS, Mom!"

Kai just smiled and continued her gaze across the entire beach.

Under an umbrella that had been driven into the sand beside a palm tree, and just in front of the Marriott Resort at Poipu Beach, Kai noticed something… actually noticed *someone* rather unusual.

There in a low-sitting azure beach chair sat a beautiful lady. She had striking features that would have been the envy of most women. Kai, however, never really considered herself part of the *most* women group. She preferred to dance to the rhythm of her own music.

11

That being said, even she was impressed.

Kai was guessing that the lady was a little older than her… maybe in her late forties or so.

The lady was well prepared, of course, and had all of the necessary supplies to enjoy her day. Kai could see her bright-blue beach towel, her turquoise-colored hat, her dark sunglasses, and a cooler from which she was pulling out a thermos and pouring a colorful red drink into what looked to be a plastic martini glass. The lady put an umbrella into the glass, brought it to her lips and took her first sip.

"Ahhhh," she seemed to say.

Kai wasn't a great lip reader, but she didn't really need to be in order to see that the lady was truly savoring her drink.

The woman appeared to be waiting on someone, because she had an identical chair beside her that was unoccupied.

None of those things were really all that unusual.

But what happened next… now *that* was unusual.

As Kai watched closely, the lady took off her hat and revealed a rich and lovely cascade of blue hair! The tone of her flowing coif actually coordinated perfectly with the color of her beach chair. It was not the kind of hue often worn by teenagers as they walked through the mall. Instead, it was an obviously intentional and very well done balayage of blue.

Strokes of darker blue mixed in with medium and lighter blues.

Kai grinned and said, "I don't know if I would've done that."

"Done what?" Michaela replied.

Kai nodded in the direction of the lady, showing Michaela what she was seeing. "That."

Michaela thought for a second, and said, "I don't know, Mom, I kinda like it. It might look good on you too!"

Kai again pulled her sunglasses down to the end of her nose as she looked at her daughter.

"Uhh. No. Granted, it does look well done and nice on her... sort of. But... uh... no."

"Come on, Mom. Live a little!" Michaela said, as she gave her mom an impish grin.

As the two of them watched the scene unfold, another woman walked up and joined the lady with the blue hair. This woman wasn't dressed in beach attire — which certainly seemed out of place. She was dressed in casual attire. It even had a bit of a business flair. It almost looked as though she was working, rather than coming to enjoy a day at the beach.

The lady with the blue hair motioned for her "working friend" to sit down next to her.

Unusual indeed. I'd like to know the rest of the story on this. Seems like the beginning of a good mystery novel.

The two ladies were obviously friendly, and it seemed to Kai that they must have known each other for some time. Kai wasn't close enough to hear what they were saying, but the conversation seemed to go back and forth from funny and laughing to serious and detailed several times.

Michaela said, "Let's go get into the water, Mom!"

Kai agreed, and they walked out into the surf, first only allowing their ankles to become covered with water.

"That's a little cold, don't you think?"

"Come on, Mom! You'll get used to it!"

They walked out a little farther until the water came up to Kai's thighs and Michaela's waist.

"Look how clear this water is!" said Kai.

"It is so beautiful!"

As they both looked down at their toes, and wiggled them on the ocean floor, Kai could hear a sound getting louder and louder off to her left.

Kai and Michaela looked up at the same time, then looked out toward the surf, and then back to each other.

"Oh no!" they yelled together.

A wave about five feet tall broke right where they were standing and knocked them squarely on their backsides.

They were drenched.

Laughing, Kai said, "Well, I guess I'm used to the water temperature now!"

Both giggled and wiped the water from their faces.

Kai glanced back up at the beach. There she saw the lady with the blue hair standing up and talking to the other woman. The two hugged and said goodbye.

Michaela said, "Mom, I'm ready to get out for a while. How about you?"

"That sounds like a good plan to me. It's getting close to lunch time. Do you want to go back to our condo? Or would you rather go into town and have something there?"

"Can we go to Holo Holo Grill again? I love that place."

"Sure. That's good with me."

As Kai and Michaela packed up their belongings, Kai again looked over toward the lady with the blue hair.

Another woman had joined her. This woman was dressed a little more casual, but still not in a swimsuit or anything Kai would have considered traditional beach wear.

Okay, now my interest is really piqued. I wonder what is going on with the lady with the blue hair.

Kai didn't realize it yet, but her curiosity about this woman would forever change her life.

Who knew?

3

Kai was awake.

Well, at least she was mostly awake.

She lie in bed, with her eyes closed, just trying to think of nothing.

Absolutely nothing.

The wonderfully aromatic wisps of freshly brewed Kona coffee drifted into her bedroom, across the floor and then fragrantly hovered above her face like the warmth from a fireplace in a mountain cabin. She smiled and slowly took a long, deep breath, still keeping her eyes closed.

Kona coffee was her favorite. Although you could order it from anywhere, the only place it was grown was on the big island of Hawaii, near the Mauna Loa and Hualalai Mountains. She and Michael had toured some of the farms where the beans are grown. When back in north Texas, they would order their coffee directly from one of the farms they toured instead of buying from the local stores back home. Ordering straight from the source ensured that she would not be getting one of those "imitation Kona coffees" that only contained ten-percent of the real beans. That was a lesson she and

Michael had learned years ago. There was a definite difference in flavor.

Michael would almost always make the coffee in the morning.

At one point, early in their marriage, it had been a bit of a bone of contention for him that Kai never wanted to make the coffee.

It wasn't so much that he really minded making it. The grinding of the beans, pouring the water into the reservoir and standing there watching the delicious black elixir slowly flow down into the pot was even somewhat relaxing to him. He just thought it would be nice if she did the job now and again.

One early morning, Michael walked into their kitchen and saw Kai sitting quietly at the kitchen table. She was preparing to read her Bible and having a little quiet time before starting her day.

Michael looked over toward the coffee pot, noticing that no coffee had been made, and said in bit of a snippy way, "Would it hurt you to make the coffee occasionally?"

Kai didn't respond to his tone in kind. Instead, she pleasantly said, "No, honey. The Bible says that you should make the coffee."

Michael said, "What the heck are you talking about?" getting even more annoyed.

"Come over here, and I'll show you!"

Kai opened her Bible like an excited child in a Sunday school class who knew the answer to the question the teacher had just asked and was overly eager to share the verse in front of the other kids.

Michael walked to the kitchen table and looked over her shoulder.

"See!" she pointed. "It says '*He*brews!'"

Michael stood there for a moment and then burst into laughter. He never complained about making the coffee again. "After all," he would say, "it's biblical!"

Kai had just heard the *He*brews joke the day before. She couldn't wait for Michael to drop a little comment about her making the coffee so that she could lovingly make him the focus of the story. She knew the time would come. She just didn't know how long she'd have to wait.

It only took one day!

That was a God thing! she thought, as she laughed at the memory and filled her lungs once more with the scent of this morning's fresh brew.

Kai knew that soon, Michael would sneak into the bedroom and bring her a cup of that wonderful coffee which had been teasing her. He would set it on her nightstand and softly kiss her forehead… nudging her to wake up for the day.

Wait.

No, he's not.

She opened her eyes and remembered that wasn't going to happen this morning… or on any future morning.

Oh, how she missed him.

Kai reluctantly forced herself to sit up and roll her legs to the side, bringing her feet softly to the floor. What she really wanted to do was lie back down, grab the pillow that was on the unused side of the bed… on Michael's side… and cry.

Instead, she slid her house slippers onto her feet and wiggled her toes.

I wonder when I started that habit of wiggling my toes? It must have begun when I was a child.

Some kids cuddled their stuffed animals. Some kids carried their blankets and pacifiers.

Kai wiggled her toes.

On the carpet. In her shoes. In the sand.

She wiggled her toes.

I still do it.

She arose and walked into the kitchen of the condo. Lindsay had been the one to make that first pot of coffee.

"Hello, Sleepyhead."

Kai laughed. "You're one to talk. I remember that you would sleep for half the day when we were in college."

"I know. I always liked to get up at 'the crack of noon' when I could. Especially on the weekends. But now… all of this 'adulting' has gotten me waking up early like my dad."

Kai and Lindsay had been best friends since their last year of high school. They met when Kai's family moved to Denton, Texas, because of her dad being transferred to the Naval Air Station Joint Reserve Base–Fort Worth. Denton was a pretty long drive from the base, but her dad wanted their family to be a bit removed from the Dallas-Fort Worth metroplex. Denton had good schools, plenty of fun things to do, and the University of North Texas brought a college-town vibe of great music, food and sports.

Lindsay was quite friendly and she immediately made Kai feel welcomed from the first day they met.

After graduating high school, they became roommates in college at the University of North Texas, and they had remained close ever since.

Lindsay was even Kai's maid of honor when she and Michael got married.

Kai was glad that Lindsay had suggested coming along on their trip to Kauai. She was glad to have the support.

"There's no sense in you going on the trip alone. I've wanted to see Kauai ever since I first heard you and Michael talking about how much you loved it. Why don't I go and keep you company?" she had told Kai.

At first, Kai resisted. But she quickly agreed and was glad that she had done so.

As the two ladies sat around the kitchen table and enjoyed their coffee, a sleepy ten year old with tousled hair and a stuffed animal walked in and sat down at the table.

"Coffee, please."

Kai replied, "With cream and sugar?"

"Cream only, like Dad drank his."

Kai and Lindsay exchanged glances.

"Nice try. But no. You know you can't have coffee at age ten."

"I know, I know." said Michaela. "I'm not fifteen yet and it'll make my feet stink."

Lindsay looked over at Kai with a puzzled look.

"What?"

"It's true," said Kai smiling. "When she'd want a sip of her dad's coffee, Michael would always tell her, 'You can't have coffee before you are at least fifteen. It will make your feet stink.' Then he would offer to let her smell his feet as proof of his point."

Michaela laughed and said, "It was pretty gross."

"You actually did it?" asked Lindsay.

"No. But just the thought!"

Shuddering, all three exclaimed in unison, "Ick!"

"His feet didn't really stink, you know?" said Kai.

"I know, Mom. I'm not a kid."

Lindsay laughed and said, "You're not? What are you then? I was definitely a kid at age ten."

"Me too," added Kai.

"Come on, ladies. I'm almost eleven. I'm over a decade old now. I'm not a kid and I'm not a teenager. You can call me a *tweenager*!"

Laughing, Kai asked, "Well what do you think that a tweenager would enjoy doing today?"

"I'm glad you asked, Mom. I've been reading about this. I'd really like to go to the Jurassic Kahili Ranch and to Manawaiopuna Falls and see where they filmed the movie, *Jurassic Park*."

Sometimes you sound so grown up. I'm not sure I'm ready for that to happen.

Kai said, "Honey, I was kind of thinking about having another day on the beach."

"If you're okay with it, I'll take her." said Lindsay. "I'd like to see those places too."

"Are you sure?"

"Of course she's sure, Mom. We'll be okay."

Lindsay quickly agreed.

"Alright then. That's the plan. You girls can go see where dinosaurs munch on movie stars, and I'll relax on the beach as I watch where sharks snack on surfers!"

"It'll be like a scary episode of National Geographic!" said Lindsay, as the girls laughed.

Before long, Lindsay and Michaela were on their way, and Kai was gathering her things to head out to the beach.

Once on the beach, Kai removed her flip-flops and wiggled her toes in the sand. She immediately began to feel the tension and worry leave her body. That was Poipu. It somehow always had this magical effect on her soul. Whenever life seemed to be chaotic and unmanageable, the sounds and surf would carry her to a different frame of mind that was wonderfully peaceful for her.

Kai got settled in and picked out one of her books from her beach bag. She pulled out her water bottle, took a sip, and began to read.

The beach was a little less crowded and a little more quiet than the day before. So it wasn't long before the rhythm of the waves and the sound of the wind relaxed her state of mind, causing her eyes to slowly close and her book to fall gently onto her chest.

After some time, a beachball came bouncing over toward her and landed in her lap, waking her up.

"Sorry 'bout that," said one of the kids playing nearby.

Kai smiled at the boy and said, "No worries. I needed to wake up anyway."

Looking at the color of her skin, Kai guessed that she had been asleep for a couple of hours.

I'll be using the aloe vera tonight.

She picked up her phone to see the time. She smiled as she saw the lock-screen photo. It was one of her favorites. It was a picture of Kai, Michael, and Michaela at a cookout at the house of one of their neighbors, the Markhams. Michael's company had built a beautiful gazebo in the Markham's back yard, and this particular dinner was in celebration of that accomplishment.

I love this picture.

The picture had been taken just a couple of months before Michael got sick. The three of them looked so happy… because they were.

The time was getting close to noon, and Kai was getting hungry.

One of her favorite things to do when on Kauai was to visit the many great food trucks in the area. The food was almost always amazing, the price was great and the experience was one to remember.

As she stood and looked around, she saw a food truck that she hadn't noticed before. It was, as so many things are in Hawaii, bright orange, yellow, and blue. It had a line of people leading up to the window and a few tables and chairs scattered around. Kai crossed the road and got in line.

When it was her turn, she quickly said to the man behind the counter, "I'll have two tacos — one fish and one shrimp. Add cilantro, pickled onions, radishes and your 'special sauce' please."

The man at the counter gave her a big smile.

"Hey, *sistah*! What's the rush? Slow down a little. You're on Hawaii time now. I'm Mack. Welcome to my food truck."

He was obviously friendly and probably flirting. She always wanted the former. But she really wasn't in the mood for the latter.

"You know? You're so right, Mack." she said with a smile. "Would you make mine a little slower than the rest? I could use the quiet time."

He laughed and said, "Yes ma'am. Coming up. What's the name?"

"Rita," she said, not wanting this friendly fellow to have her real name.

I have no idea why I did that. It's not like I'll see him again.

Kai smiled, paid for her order and found a chair just off the concrete pad and under a shade tree. She sat down to wait on her food.

Scanning her eyes across the area, her attention came to rest on a familiar sight.

There she was.

It was the lady with the blue hair.

She's changed her outfit, but not that hair.

Kai smirked to herself, hoping that her thoughts didn't make their way to her face.

The lady had pretty much staged her venue similar to the day before. She had the two azure chairs, her food from the truck, and she was talking to a woman sitting in the seat beside her.

This time, not only was the lady with the blue hair's guest not in beach attire, she was in a business suit! She wore a cream-colored ruched blouse that flowed from her left shoulder to the right side of her waist. That was paired with a lightweight double-meshed skirt with small black palms overlaying a light pink under layer.

The two ladies conversed as Kai got comfortable in her chair and began to sip on a bottle of water.

The lady with the blue hair glanced over toward Kai and smiled.

Kai smiled back and then looked away.

That's embarrassing! I hope she doesn't think I'm eavesdropping or stalking her.

Kai's thoughts were interrupted by the man in the truck.

"Order up for Rita!"

Kai walked to the window and picked up her tacos.

"Thanks, Mack."

As she turned to walk back to her chair, she noticed that a man and a boy, father and son she assumed, had claimed her spot.

Seeing that they were already eating their lunch, she surveyed the venue, looking for another place to sit.

The lady in the blue hair was saying goodbye to her guest. Seeing Kai's predicament, she smiled and waved her over.

"You're welcome to join me if you like. The place is a little crowded today."

Uncomfortable at first, Kai replied, "Thank you. But I don't want to be a bother."

"You'll be no bother at all. I would enjoy the company."

Kai accepted her offer and walked over to her.

"Well, hi Rita. I'm Belle."

Kai eased down into the chair and said, "I'm a little embarrassed. My name isn't Rita. It's Kai."

"Why did Mack call you Rita?"

"Because that's the name I gave him," Kai said, blushing a bit.

"I thought he was flirting, so I made up a name."

Belle laughed.

"Don't feel bad. His real name isn't Mack either."

"It isn't?"

"No. His real name is actually Makanui. It means *prince born in the eye of greatness*."

"Really? Well Mack is much closer to Makanui than Rita is to Kai."

Both ladies laughed.

Belle said, "That is true indeed."

"By the way, are you aware of the meaning of the name Kai?" asked Belle.

"No. I never thought to ask. My parents love coming to Hawaii. I just assumed it had something to do with the islands."

Belle said, "It does indeed. In Europe, Kai means 'warrior.' But here on the islands, Kai means 'sea.' So you could be a warrior of great strength, or a beautiful turbulent ocean who is a powerful force of nature."

Kai smiled and said, "I don't really feel like much of a warrior lately. But that turbulent ocean part hits pretty close to home."

Kai saw a gentle look of compassion in Belle's eyes.

Wanting to take the focus of the conversation off of herself, Kai asked, "So, what does the name Belle mean?"

Oh, I would love to ask if it means "ding-a-ling!" Boy, Michael's corny one-liners have really warped my sense of humor over the years.

Belle replied, "Well now… my full name is Bellarosa. It is Italian for 'beautiful rose.'"

"I like that!"

"My parents loved Italy. Bellarosa was the name of one of their friends over there."

"It's beautiful!"

"I agree!" Belle said with a look of pride. "I lived in Italy for a couple of years, and being an American girl with an Italian name made me quite popular."

"I would imagine so."

"It didn't work as well when I was a teenager and we returned to the States. We settled in Brenham, Texas, the home of a very popular ice cream brand called Blue Bell."

"I actually live in Texas," said Kai. "I know Blue Bell ice cream well. It's my favorite brand."

Belle continued, "It's good ice cream, but as a young teenager I would often be teased by the other kids. 'Your parents loved ice cream so much that they named you Bell! Blue Bell!'

"I would say, 'My name's not Bell! It... is... Bellarosa!' But it made no difference."

Belle smiled as she thought about the teasing.

"It bothered me then. I was at an age where all I needed was one more reason to feel self-conscious. Now it's more of a pleasant memory."

"Do you live here on Kauai now?"

"I do. I came here on a vacation ten years ago and just decided to stay. I determined that if the chickens can just show up and stay, so could I."

One of the unique things about the island of Kauai is that chickens roam freely. It's not at all unusual to be awakened by the sound of a rooster just outside your window. You may even find a hen resting in a chair on your lanai. When you find the occasional egg underneath her, it can spark childhood memories of Easter baskets, family gatherings, and church socials.

"I saw one crossing the road in front of our condo yesterday," said Kai. "I wanted to ask him, 'Why did you cross the road? I really want to know the answer.'"

The ladies laughed.

Kai said, "I'm sure he ran off, clucking to the other chickens, saying, 'Wow! That was original!'"

Belle said, "Or maybe he pulled out his little rooster phone and texted his other little rooster buddies, 'WTC???'"

Kai gave Belle a bewildered look.

Belle tilted her head and raised her hands to the side, palms up: "What the cluck?"

Both ladies laughed… "cackled," so to speak.

"That was so corny! It sounded like something my husband would've said!"

Belle asked, "So, are you here with your husband? I saw you and a girl that I assumed was your daughter yesterday, but didn't notice anyone else."

Kai's smile dimmed just a little.

"No. My husband, Michael, my daughter, Michaela, and I have been coming to Kauai every December for eight years now."

She looked down and paused.

"Michael died unexpectedly back in May of this year."

"Oh, Kai. I'm so sorry."

Kai didn't speak at first. She just nodded her head and attempted a smile.

"I decided to still come this year. It was a difficult choice to make at first, but I'm glad I did. Michaela really seemed to need the trip, and my friend Lindsay came along with me so I wouldn't feel so alone."

"Are you married?" asked Kai.

"No. I was married once. But after a while I came to realize that he and I both wanted different things that just couldn't work together.

He loved to go camping and hiking and wanted to live off the grid. I didn't. I wanted to be able to build my business and allow myself to be pampered just a bit by having such luxuries as… oh… I don't know… electricity."

"I like electricity, too!" Kai said with a smile.

"So, one day we had a long talk, and came to the mutual decision that we should go our separate ways. So, I took him to the edge of the forest and I 'released him into the wild!'"

Kai laughed.

"I've been single ever since. I do date. But I date in a very environmentally friendly manner. I am strictly a 'catch and release' woman, when it comes to men."

Both ladies laughed.

"That's hysterical!" said Kai.

Belle continued. "Kai, I've read that talking about lost loved ones can be quite helpful when you're going through the grieving process. If you'd like to share it with me, I'd love to hear the story of you and Michael."

Kai was so surprised by Belle. She wasn't at all like what Kai expected when she first saw "the lady with the blue hair."

She was comforting. She was perceptive. She was beautiful.

And yes… she had blue hair.

"If I start taking up too much time, please feel welcome to tell me to stop."

"Not at all. I have no more appointments today. I'm all ears."

No more appointments? Interesting.

"Michael and I met my senior year in college."

She smiled as she reminisced. "He was so handsome! He had blue eyes, brown hair, and the greatest smile.

"He was really mature for a man of his age, too. Most college guys seemed to treat dating like a sport. They were always on the hunt, and often made girls feel more like prey or trophies, rather than people. That was a complete turn off for me. But Michael was different. He was studying to be an architect, and by the time we met, he'd already started a small construction business. He would build decks and landscapes. After graduating, he just kept growing that business and eventually became a highly sought after outdoor design and construction expert. His ability to transform a simple backyard into an absolutely incredible family space was amazing."

Belle said nothing. She just listened.

"I think maybe working for a living as he finished his degree made him 'grow up' faster than other boys his age. He was thoughtful. He was also a little shy back then. He treated me with such respect. He always wanted to know what I thought and how I perceived life. He always believed in me and my ability to accomplish anything.

"We got married after dating for a couple of years, and almost immediately got the news that Michaela was on the way. She was born exactly eleven months, to the day, after our wedding. Financially, we didn't need me to work, so I became a stay-at-home mom and took care of our household. That was all wonderful in so many ways. But now that he's gone, I don't feel prepared to make a living for Michaela and myself."

"What about the business? Could you take that over?"

"Actually, Michael added a partner a few years ago. Their agreement basically said that if either one of them died, the business would go to the partner who was still living. They'd bought an insurance policy that provided the proceeds to purchase the deceased partner's half of the business from his spouse."

"That's good."

Kai continued, "Yes. We aren't in financial danger. But I still need to find a way to make a living. I'm unprepared. I'm scared. And I miss him being there to remind me how much he believes in me and that I can make it all happen."

The two ladies sat quietly for a while.

Kai broke the silence.

"Enough about me. Tell me your story. And please start by telling me about your blue hair."

Belle laughed.

"Oh. You noticed that?"

"I did! I thought it matched your chairs quite well when I first saw you yesterday on the beach," Kai said with a chuckle.

"I think that's why I picked these chairs," Belle said as she brushed the fabric. "I decided to have my hair colored blue about six months ago."

"Wait! Are you telling me that you're not a natural bluehead?" Kai asked as they both laughed. "I'm amazed!"

Belle smiled and said, "Only my hairdresser knows for sure. Actually, with the world seeming to be in so much turmoil over the last few years, I found myself becoming more and more judgmental. I would prejudge people and situations before having enough information… or even having any information. And one of the most valuable lessons I learned building my business is to ask questions, consider things from the other person's perspective, and offer solutions if I have them.

"I was having coffee one morning, thinking about how I needed to change my direction on that issue, when a couple of teenage girls came into the coffee shop."

"With blue hair?" asked Kai.

"You guessed it! With blue hair. As I drank my coffee, I found myself thinking some not-so-flattering things about two young ladies whom I had never even met. I knew nothing about them."

Kai looked a little embarrassed, and said, "Well, if it's confession time, I probably did a little of that myself… yesterday… with you."

Belle laughed and said, "I get it. But there I sat… thinking about how I needed to stop being so judgmental… while being judgmental."

"Habits are hard to break." said Kai.

"Yes they are. So I decided right there to do something unusual to remind myself to change my behavior. I called my hair stylist and told him what I wanted to do, and I drove directly to his shop before I could change my mind."

Belle tilted her head and shook her hair as she fluffed it with her hand like a model in a hair-care product commercial.

"The results are in. My hair is blue."

Kai said, "Well, yours definitely doesn't look like what I've seen on teenage girls."

Belle smiled and said, "Hey! I still wanted to have my own style!"

"Has it helped?"

"Yes, it has. Now, when I find myself prejudging people, or thinking that I have all of the right answers, I can catch a glance at my reflection and say to myself, '"Said the lady with the blue hair.'"

"I love that!" said Kai. "I think that's brilliant!"

"Thank you!"

"Belle, what's your business? I've noticed you 'holding court' with a few ladies yesterday and today. Do they work for you?"

"Oh no. They're some of my clients. My protégés."

"Clients? Protégés?"

"Yes."

"I built a very successful direct sales business over the last twenty-five years. Although I had no experience in sales or in running any business—much less my own—it has provided a great life for me."

"Wow! I don't think I could be in sales. The thought makes me uncomfortable."

"That's what I thought in the beginning too. Fortunately, I didn't let that stop me. Now, I have one of the largest sales teams in the world."

"That's great! Are those ladies you were meeting with part of your sales team?"

"No. They're ladies that are in the process of building their careers. Some are in sales. Some aren't. But they all have one thing in common."

"What's that?"

"They are women who are committed to building great lives for themselves and their families."

"Are they single mothers, like me?"

"Some are. Not all. But they all want to grow a career or a business so that, whether they're in a relationship or alone, they're never unprepared for the future."

"I can relate to that." said Kai.

"I still earn my living from my direct sales business. But a few years ago, I began an additional business. I coach and mentor ladies.

Those you saw live here in Kauai, and came to spend a little time with me on their lunch breaks at work."

"That explains something. I was a little confused about their choices for beach attire."

Belle laughed and said, "Did you judge them for it? Do you need the number for my hairdresser?"

"No. More curious than judgmental."

Kai smiled. "Well… at least about them."

"It's funny," replied Belle, "My clients that are on the mainland are always in swimsuits when we get to meet in person. But my local clients are almost always dressed for work."

"How do you work with clients on the mainland?"

"We still get face to face. We just use our computers to do so. Many of them will fly out once per year so that we can have an in-person session."

"What a great business trip!" said Kai.

Belle thought for a couple of minutes and then asked a question.

"Kai, I'd like for you to consider something."

"What?"

"As you're making this transition, I would like to mentor you and help you navigate the things you'll be facing."

"How much would it cost?"

"Actually, in this case, rather than having you as a client, I'd like to do so as your friend. I usually pick one person each year and mentor them just because I want to do so, and not because they are a client. It's my way of making the world a better place."

"Think about it for a bit and let me know if you're interested."

Kai looked at her watch, silently counted to ten and then enthusiastically said, "Yes! I'll take you up on your offer! Did I think about it long enough?"

After their laughter died down, Kai said, "That's very generous, Belle. Are you sure? I can certainly pay."

"Absolutely," replied Belle. "When are you heading home?"

"In a couple of days."

"Can you make time for our first session in the morning around nine?"

"Yes. On the beach?"

"Absolutely. That's my favorite office!"

"See you there!"

It was late afternoon when Lindsay and Michaela returned from their outing. Kai had begun preparing dinner. She was chopping vegetables for a nice salad. There were hearts of romaine lettuce, onions, radishes, carrots, red and yellow bell peppers, and fresh pineapple.

On a plate beside the cutting board was a filet of wild-caught ahi tuna, fresh from the local seafood market. She had rubbed it in olive oil, seasoned it lightly with salt, and rolled it in a blanket of crushed black peppercorns.

"Oh, Mom! You should've seen it! That waterfall was amazing!"

"Sounds like you two had a blast!"

"We did!"

"It was a little scary when that helicopter we were riding in had the engine go out! But other than that, it was a blast!"

Kai said, "What???!!!" and shot her eyes over at Lindsay with a look of panic. "You took her on a helicopter ride? And the engine went out?"

Lindsay laughed.

"No, Kai. She's kidding!"

"Whew! You had me going for a second!"

Lindsay replied, "The engine only sputtered!"

Michaela burst out into laughter.

"Mom, we wouldn't do that without asking you first! You would've had a complete meltdown."

"That's true," replied Kai.

Lindsay and Michaela asked in unison, "So can we do it tomorrow?"

"Your sense of humor is becoming so grown up," replied Kai. "And, no. But you can grab the dishes and start setting the table. Let's eat out on the lanai."

"Will do."

Kai finished cutting the vegetables, and took the plate with the tuna to the grill out on the lanai. Lindsay followed.

Kai seemed different. She seemed to have a little more spring in her step and a little more of a smile in her eyes this evening.

Lindsay asked, "So what did you do today? You seem a bit more chipper than you were this morning."

Kai thought for a second, wrinkled her eyebrows a bit and said, "I am, aren't I? This may sound a little bit crazy."

Lindsay said, "Go ahead. I'm your best friend. If you can't sound crazy with me, where else can you go? Plus, our crazies have always matched pretty well anyway."

"Okay. I'm feeling hopeful. Or at least I am feeling more hopeful than I've felt since Michael died."

"What happened?"

Kai said, "Yesterday, Michaela and I noticed a woman on the beach. As she sat there, she had a few ladies come and visit her. Each stayed for a probably an hour or so. After they finished their conversation, each visitor left and another would take her place. It seemed odd to me at the time that none were dressed in beach attire. But instead, they were dressed in work clothes."

"Okay. Nothing to go on here yet, Kai. Help me out."

"The lady had blue hair."

"You aren't thinking about dying your hair blue, are you?"

"No," Kai said with a grin. She thought for a second and said, "At least not yet. I pretty much just mentally dismissed the scene and thought she must be some eccentric woman whose friends come by to check on her."

"I can understand that," said Lindsay. "But how is this making you feel hopeful?"

Kai frowned and said, "I'm getting there. Be patient. Today as I was having lunch at that food truck across the street from the beach, I saw her again. She was visiting with another lady as they ate. Long story short, I ended up meeting her and, although she had finished eating, we sat together while I ate my lunch."

Lindsay continued to listen.

"As it turns out, she's built a very successful business, and is a coach... a mentor to ladies who are building a career or a business that will provide well for them and their families. She helps put them into a position where they will be financially and mentally prepared to take on the world ahead."

"That sounds like something that'd be music to your ears right now."

"It was. And to think, I almost missed the opportunity to meet her because I'd completely misjudged what she would be like because of the color of her hair. She was kind. She was well-spoken. She was insightful."

Lindsay added, "And she had blue hair? What's the story on the hair?"

Kai told Lindsay the story of how Belle made the decision to dye her hair blue.

"Now, when she finds herself making judgments about people or situations, before having all of the facts, she thinks to herself, 'Said the lady with the blue hair.'

"She asked me if I would allow her to mentor me as I try to figure out what to do, career wise, going forward. I said yes."

"I think that's very cool," said Lindsay. "It'll be interesting to see how it goes. Whatever the results… it already seems to be doing good things for you."

Kai agreed.

Michaela walked out onto the lanai, bringing the salad.

"Is the tuna ready yet? I'm getting pretty hungry."

Kai turned it over on the grill one last time to check, then put it back on the plate.

"Me too. Let's eat."

The ladies enjoyed their dinner as they watched the dimming light of the sun give way to the vibrant twinkling of the stars.

Lindsay and Kai enjoyed a bottle of a 2015 Pinot Noir from a vineyard in the Napa Valley. It was one of their favorite wines.

Kai said, "I think 2015 may have been the best year yet for their Pinot."

Michaela enjoyed a glass of orange juice. Holding up the bottle, she said, "Ah. Last week. A very good year for my orange juice."

The ladies laughed and relaxed until bedtime.

Kai had the best night's sleep she had experienced in months.

4

Kai was excited to get to the beach.

Michaela and Lindsay decided to stay around the condo until Kai returned from her 9:00 appointment with Belle. Then the three of them would be taking a catamaran tour out of Poipu. The trip would include snorkeling, a picnic lunch, and seeing some of the most beautiful sights that could be found on earth. The waters around Kauai were so clear that when the boat was anchored, the rope could be seen extending from the large metal fluke on the bottom of the ocean floor all the way up to the vessel. It gave Kai the illusion that the boat was a balloon floating high in the air, tethered by a string to a weight some thirty feet below.

Kai arrived at their meeting a few minutes early as Belle was just finishing another session.

Motioning for Kai to come ahead, Belle made introductions.

"Kai, this is Whitney. She owns and operates one of the most popular wedding venues in Hawaii. People from all over the world seek her out. Not only for her venue, but for her expertise as well. She puts on some absolutely stunning weddings! She started off coordinating events for another company. But she eventually bought them out and has now become the 'go to' contact for brides wanting to have their 'together forevers' start here on Kauai."

"Hi Whitney! Nice to meet you!"

"Likewise, Kai! Nice to meet you, too!"

"Whitney, Kai is a new protégé. She is here for the week, but lives back in Texas."

Whitney nodded her head and said, "You used to live in Texas, didn't you Belle?"

"Yes, I did."

Belle continued, "Kai unfortunately became a widow a few months ago. She is now starting to navigate the course on where she needs to go next to build a future for herself and her daughter, Michaela."

Whitney said, "Oh, Kai. I am so sorry."

Kai replied, "Thank you."

"Well, as you make this transition and begin to move forward, you will never be in better hands than you are with Belle."

Belle looked a little embarrassed.

"It's the truth Belle. The advice and mentoring you gave to me made all of the difference in the world. I could have never built *Nani Mo'olelo* without your guidance."

"Kai," said Whitney, "This is a very wise move on your part!"

Kai replied, "I'm pretty excited!"

"What is Nani Mo… mole… o?" asked Kai.

Whitney laughed.

"*Nani Mo'olelo. Nani* means *beautiful*." Speaking slowly, Whitney continued, "And *Mo'olelo*… means *story*."

"*Nani Mo'olelo*." said Kai. "Beautiful story."

"That's right," said Whitney. "Spoken like a true Hawaiian. I'd love to stay and chat, but I have a busy day ahead.

"Good luck, Kai!" said Whitney as she waved and headed off the beach.

"Thanks, Whitney! Nice to meet you!"

Kai got settled into her chair, took a sip of her coffee from her travel cup and pulled out a notepad and a pen.

Belle began their session with a question.

"Kai, when you think about your life a year from now... or even five years from now, what do you want it to look like? I'm not really talking about business goals. I am talking more about how you want your life to be. Paint a word picture for me."

Kai thought for a few seconds, then answered.

"I want to have a business or career going well enough that thoughts of money don't cause stress for me. I don't have to be rich... although I certainly wouldn't turn that down."

Belle smiled.

"But I want money to be a non-issue in my life. And in whatever I do, I want to make sure that I am always available for Michaela. I want to have the freedom to be at her school functions. I want to be able to take her on trips. I want to build memories together."

Belle asked, "So what have you thought of so far in regards to a career or business you might enjoy doing that would also give you that freedom?"

"I haven't really come up with much yet. I've thought about going to work for my parents. After Dad retired from the Air Force, he opened a flight school. They have told me that I can work for them if

43

I'd like. It would be mostly clerical, I'm sure. They would be doing it only for the purpose of taking care of their 'little girl.' I don't think they really need to hire anyone right now. Although I really do appreciate the gesture, my thoughts are that it really wouldn't be the right situation for me to build a future."

"What else have you thought of?"

"Well, I have always had a special place in my heart for helping the homeless. I've considered going to work for one of the local charities that provide food, shelter, and support for them."

"I applaud your heart, Kai. It's obvious that you are a good person who has a focus on others and making the world a little better wherever you go. Have you looked into anything else?"

"No. Truthfully, I actually haven't even looked into those, with the exception of working for my parents. Come to think of it, I didn't even look into that. They approached me. What do you think I should do, Belle?"

Belle considered her question.

"Kai, the way I coach and mentor people is actually going to sound a little bit counterintuitive at first. But it's rare that I actually tell anyone what they should do."

"You don't?" said Kai, a little disappointed.

"No," said Belle with a gentle smile. "My purpose isn't to tell you what you should do. It's not to 'fix' you. Instead, my goal is to help you find these answers in yourself. To help you focus on a destination of your choosing. Then to guide you along the way so that you can build a life that makes you happy."

"Please go on," said Kai.

"If you want to build a happy life for you and Michaela, the first thing you should remember is that whatever you choose to do in a career or business must match the values you hold most dearly. For example, you could build a great business that brings enormous financial rewards. But if in doing so, you found yourself in a position where you were missing events that are important to you and Michaela, or if you found that you just were not having the freedom you said you wanted in order to spend the time with her in traveling, etc., you would find yourself feeling hollow inside. Your financial worries may be gone. But you wouldn't really be happy."

"That makes sense," said Kai. "So does that mean that I have to choose between earning a lot of money, or being happy spending time with Michaela?"

"Not at all. It's not an either-or proposition. It simply means that you first decide what your values are. Decide on the things that you hold most dearly. Then make decisions on what you do going forward that are congruent with those values.

"If I were to ask you to name your top five priorities in life… to name the five things you place the most value on, what would your answers be?"

"Michaela would be the top priority, without a doubt. Then, I have to find a way to generate an income. I want to feel self-sufficient."

"Go on." said Belle.

Kai continued, "The next three would probably be to be able to be there for my parents as they get older. I don't think they will need me financially. But they will need my physical and emotional support as they age. Then I would like to be able to help others. That's why I was thinking about working for a homeless charity.

"I'm not sure I can think of a fifth one right now."

Belle said, "That's okay. This will be a work in progress. I would like to see you come up with at least five over the next few days. Over time, you may find that these priorities will change, and that is perfectly alright. Expected, even. But as you go forward making your decisions, keeping your focus on the priorities that you value the most can help you avoid making a lot of mistakes along the way.

"As you think of the way you answered earlier about how you want your life to be five years from now — and you compare that with the career possibilities that you mentioned of going to work for your parents, or going to work for a homeless charity, how well do you think they match up?"

Kai answered, "Working for my parents would most likely give me the schedule freedom that I want to be able to be at Michaela's school functions. But it wouldn't provide enough income to be able to do the things for her that I'd like to do."

Belle said, "I heard someone once define being wealthy as having enough time to enjoy your money and enough money to enjoy your time. That is really true when you think about it, and it doesn't matter what your income level is. If you can do both of those things, you are truly wealthy."

"I can see that," said Kai. "Working at the charity, while it would feel very rewarding, probably wouldn't give me enough money or time."

"You're right, I'm sure."

Belle continued. "Kai, I am going to teach you a series of rules that I use to help protégés as they grow and find their direction."

Belle started laughing, thinking about what she had just said. "Rules! That sentence is actually hilarious when you consider how much of a rule breaker I can be at times," she said, fluffing her blue

46

hair. "But, nonetheless, these rules have helped me build my business and they have also helped my clients and protégés do the same.

"The first rule is called *The Stewardess Rule*. I know that they are called flight-attendants now, but I am a little old fashioned and am at times reluctant to change."

Belle laughed and said, "Rule breaker! What did I tell you? I'm a rule breaker!"

Kai laughed as well.

"So, what is *The Stewardess Rule*?" Kai asked.

Belle answered, "Do you listen to the flight attendants when they are making their announcements in preparation for takeoff?"

Kai answered, "It's a little embarrassing. But yes, I know those announcements well. Too well. I can be a little bit 'over-studious' at times."

Belle smiled.

"What do they say about oxygen masks?"

Kai answered in her best flight-attendant voice.

"In the unlikely event of cabin decompression, an oxygen mask will automatically drop in front of you. To start the flow of oxygen, pull the mask towards you. Place it firmly over your nose and mouth, secure the elastic band behind your head, and breathe normally. Although the bag does not inflate, oxygen is flowing to the mask. If you are traveling with a child or someone who requires assistance, secure your oxygen mask first before attempting to assist others. Keep your mask on until a uniformed crew member advises you to remove it."

"Oh my! You weren't kidding, were you?"

They both laughed.

Belle lifted her finger, smiled and said, "True story. I was traveling in Europe a few years ago. The airline announcements there were pretty much the same as they are here. But on one particular flight, the stewardess... I mean *flight-attendant* was very creative. When making the part of the announcement that regarded putting the mask on a child, she said, 'If you are traveling with a child, secure your mask first, and then assist your child. If traveling with more than one child, please select your favorite child at this time.'"

"Oh my goodness! You have to be kidding!" Kai was laughing hysterically.

"Not kidding. Most of the people on the plane were not even paying attention. However, I was. And the flight attendant and I were making eye contact when she said it. The rest of the plane was silent, and suddenly I broke out into laughter.

"Did everyone look at the flight attendant who had made the hilarious comment? No! They all turned and looked at me! She later brought me a free drink. She told me that she says that on every flight, just to see who is paying attention."

"That is too funny!"

Belle returned to her point. "The reason that you need to put your oxygen mask on first is so that you don't pass out as you're trying to help someone else... putting you both at risk."

Kai said, "That makes sense. You're no good to anybody if you pass out."

Belle said, "That same principle applies in many areas of life. Before you can help someone else, you have to help yourself first."

"The Stewardess Rule is secure your own oxygen mask before attempting to assist others.

"Once you get your feet on solid financial ground, then you can support multiple charities that are close to your heart."

Kai nodded. "Good point."

"My business is in direct sales. The same lesson applied in my case as I began to build a team of people. Once I knew what I was doing, then I was able to help others by teaching them to do the same."

Belle put her hand on Kai's shoulder, lowered her voice, and said, "The same also applies to how you and Michaela will get through the coming months and years. You have to make sure that you are working on your grief and your pain, so that you are able to help Michaela with hers. You'll be going through this at the same time. But don't neglect to take care of your needs as you also help her do the same."

Kai's eyes began to fill with tears. She looked at Belle and gently nodded.

The two ladies sat quietly for a couple of minutes.

Belle broke the silence. "To earn the income you need and still have the freedom you want, you're most likely going to be working for yourself in some capacity. Even then, you still need to make choices that align with your values. I've had friends who thought they owned businesses. But in fact, it was the other way around. Their businesses owned them."

"You mentioned that you didn't think you could be in direct sales," Belle said as she was thinking through the possibilities. "Why is that?"

Kai answered, "The idea of selling anything makes me feel pretty uneasy. I remember being in the band program when I was in school. We often did fundraisers. Sometimes we sold candy. Other times, we sold wrapping paper. But the whole idea made me uncomfortable.

"I didn't do very well."

49

Belle said, "I can relate. I felt the same way as I began my business. Have you ever wondered why you felt that way?"

"Not really. I never thought about it."

"I have a theory about that," Belle continued.

"When you look at the history of salespeople as portrayed in movies, or unfortunately at times even in real life, the image you find is often not very flattering. It's the snake-oil salesman. It's that pushy, 'get your foot inside the door' image that no good person would ever want to resemble."

"Now that you mention it," said Kai, "I remember my dad getting annoyed with a vacuum-cleaner salesman that just didn't seem to take no for an answer. He got really ticked!"

"Bingo! It could be that this 'poor excuse for a salesman,' who left a very bad first impression, has framed how you see all salespeople. Later, that image likely carried over into your fundraising program for your band. You didn't like that salesperson. Your dad didn't like that salesperson. Maybe all salespeople are like that.

"Then there you were… candy in hand… trying to be one of those things. You know… a *salesperson*!" Belle said with a fake shudder. "You were trying to be something that you, and maybe even more importantly, your dad, didn't like. That would be tough on anyone."

"I see your point," said Kai.

"Let me ask you a question, Kai. When you think of me, do you put me in the same category with that vacuum-cleaner salesman?"

"Of course not. You're different."

Belle laughed. "It's the hair, right? I'm different because of the hair."

Kai laughed too.

"No. You're different because you listen. You're kind. You're helpful."

"I'm also in sales, Kai," said Belle. "I started by just selling products. Then later I began to build a team. That was selling as well. I sold career opportunities."

Kai replied, "I don't really think of you as a salesperson at all."

"Knowing the frame which has formed your idea of what a salesperson is… I take that as a wonderful compliment. But let's see if we can change that frame and give you a different picture of what a salesperson should be. Salespeople are actually some of the most important linchpins in our economy."

"What do you mean?"

Belle explained.

"Many people think of the economy as a 'pie.' I'm sure you've heard the phrase, 'Go get your slice of the pie!' That phrase is usually used by people to encourage you to chase your goals and live your dreams. But the trouble with the pie analogy is that when a piece of pie is eaten by one person, it can't be eaten by another. And the supply of slices in a pie are limited.

"I prefer to think of the economy as a relay race. It's not about eating a slice of pie. Instead, success comes when the baton passes… or the money changes hands from one person to the next."

"Keep going," said Kai. "I think I understand, but I need a little help."

"Okay. When I earn money, I may go spend it at the grocery store. The grocery store owner then spends some of that money to send her children to daycare. Some of the money goes to their employees and their suppliers. Those people then spend money at restaurants, or on cars, etc.

"Every time that money changed hands, someone received value that made their life a little better. My real point is that the more often we can make money change hands from one person to the next, the better everyone does. And one of the most crucial ways that money changes hands, and this relay process continues, is when a salesperson makes a sale."

"Okay. I understand. But how is that going to help me see salespeople in a different light? I see that they are necessary. But that doesn't necessarily make me feel much more comfortable about becoming one of them."

Belle replied, "Kai, most salespeople… all of the really great ones… are actually just like you and me. They are kind. They care about people and treat them with respect. Those few who aren't like that give the rest a bad reputation.

"I want you to do a mental exercise for me. Think about a product that you have owned and really loved. One that did exactly what it was supposed to do and did it so well that you found yourself telling your friends about it."

Kai thought for a second and said, "Okay. I've got one."

"Now with that product in mind, think about this. A truly great salesperson never tries to talk anyone into buying anything. Instead, they find someone who has a specific need. They find a company that has a solution to that need. They put the two together—and for doing so they get paid.

"When you told your friends about that product. Were you excited?"

"Yes."

"Did they buy the same product?"

"Some did."

"That is exactly what a great salesperson does.

"A friend of mine defines 'selling' as finding *very real* people with *very real* needs, and putting them together with a *very real* company that has the solution for those needs. If those factors are in place, the process becomes comfortable for both you and your prospect. You're simply helping people get together. Then you get paid for making the connection."

"I'm starting to see what you mean," said Kai. "That sounds a little like being a 'professional matchmaker!'" she said, smiling.

"That is a great analogy, Kai! And if you put things in motion for two people to become a great couple, you wouldn't feel uncomfortable. You would feel happy and excited, right?"

"Right!"

"That's the same thought process that makes someone a great salesperson. If you approach things that way, a sales career will align with your values. It will reflect how you think people should behave toward each other. Then it's just a matter of learning your skills."

Hearing Michael's voice softly in the back of her mind, Kai said, "And I can do anything once I set my mind to it."

"We have time for one more quick rule," Belle said. "Rule number two is *The Success Rule.* You can be successful at anything in life as long as enough people know what you do."

"What do you mean?" asked Kai.

"There's a recipe for building a very successful and sustainable business. First, find a product or service that you truly believe in. Make it something that you wholeheartedly feel makes someone's life better when they own it. Something that would even give you a greater sense of self-worth by the simple fact that you helped them find it.

53

"Then do what it takes to let enough people know and understand how you can help make their lives better with your product or service. It doesn't even really matter how much that product or service costs, as long as the buyer's life becomes better because they own it.

"If you make ten dollars when someone owns your product, and a thousand people buy that product, then you earn ten thousand dollars because you helped make their lives better. If you make a thousand dollars for your product, and a thousand people decide to buy it, then you just earned one million dollars for making their world a better place.

"Not everyone will buy. But if what you have truly makes their lives better in some way, and enough people know what you do…"

Kai completed Belle's sentence, "You can be successful at anything in life as long as enough people know what you do."

Kai continued, "That really does make sense to me. I'll have to put some more thought into the idea of some type of sales business."

"Our hour is almost up," said Belle.

Kai nodded and laughed with a little bit of a sigh. "That's a good thing. I'm feeling a little bit overwhelmed.

"Excited! But also a little overwhelmed. My mind is racing with possibilities."

Belle asked, "When do you go back to Texas?"

"We leave tomorrow."

"Okay. We will start computer calls when you get settled back in and rest up from your jet lag."

Belle stood and gave Kai a hug.

"Just so you know, Kai, that feeling of being excited and also a little overwhelmed is actually quite normal when you are starting anything new that has a lot of potential. You can see the possibilities. But since you 'don't know what you don't know' yet, it throws your system into a bit of a tizzy. Don't worry. As time goes on, you will start to develop a sense of the questions you need to ask and the skills you'll need to develop."

"At least then, I will know what I don't know," Kai laughed.

"That's right. And you won't be going through it alone. I can't do it for you. But I can certainly be here along the way."

Kai said, "I'm in. And I so appreciate your help."

"My pleasure."

Kai left the beach and headed back to her condo to meet Michaela and Lindsay. As planned, the three ladies then headed to the pier and boarded the catamaran for their excursion.

Later, as the boat stopped for some snorkeling and lunch, Lindsay asked Kai, "So, how was your meeting? Did it go well?"

"Actually, it did. I am even considering some things that I would have never considered before. It's pretty exciting! But it is also a little scary."

"Considering what?"

"I'm thinking about going into sales of some type."

"I think you would be great in sales! My dad has been in sales for his entire career. He had planned to teach. But then, as he tells the story, his children and his wife picked up some pesky habits that forced him to choose a path that brought in more money than what a teacher's salary would provide."

"What pesky habits?" asked Kai.

"Eating. Living indoors. Wearing clothes."

Laughing, Kai said, "Oh no! Michaela has developed those same pesky habits! I may have no other choice either!"

"Seriously, Kai. I think you would be a great salesperson. You'd be like my dad… one of the good guys."

Kai smiled and said, "Thanks!"

Then Kai laid back on the catamaran and enjoyed the sun and the waves.

This feels like I am about to jump out of an airplane for the first time! I hope I know what I am doing.

Kai heard a soft voice in the back of her mind.

It was Michael's voice.

It simply said, "*You've got this.*"

Even the most well-seasoned travelers will find the flight from Lihue, Hawaii, to Dallas, Texas, to be a bit of a drain on their systems.

Scratch that.

It is exhausting!

At least, Kai and Michael always found the trip exhausting.

There were never any non-stop flights from which to pick, so Kai and Michael always booked with American Airlines, taking advantage of the flight that had only one connection. They would fly first from Lihue to Honolulu. That was followed with a straight shot into the Dallas-Fort Worth International Airport. The first segment of the flight was only a short forty-five minutes or so and departed in the late afternoon. Then they would have a layover of about an hour before boarding the flight to Dallas. That leg of the flight would be about seven-and-a-half hours. But since it would be mostly overnight, sleeping made the time pass more quickly.

Easy, right?

Nope!

It was still exhausting.

Michael made it a business practice of putting all expenses on a credit card which built miles on American Airlines. He would save them all year long. Then when the family took their annual trip to Kauai, he would use the miles as a way to upgrade their seats from coach to first class.

Kai remembered Michael saying, "It's possible that I might splurge on the price of first-class tickets on a trip of this length, but I'm not so sure. I'd much rather buy a coach ticket and use the miles for the upgrade."

Kai would laugh and reply, "Oh, honey. You would pay for the ticket if you had to. Otherwise, you would get lonely sitting back there in coach while Michaela and I were in first class!"

Kai smiled as she remembered her comments. It was funny to say those things back then. But now that the financial responsibilities for her and Michaela rested solely on her shoulders, she wasn't sure that she would spend the money on that luxury either.

Fortunately, there were still plenty of miles to upgrade the three tickets for this trip. So Kai, Michaela, and Lindsay were all very well attended to for their flight home.

Once on the flight from Honolulu to Dallas, the flight attendants would bring complimentary beverages during the boarding process. They had a surprisingly good wine list, which brought smiles to Kai and Lindsay. They would bring menus with multiple selections for dinner entrees. Then, after dinner came Michaela's favorite part. There would be wonderful desserts of ice cream sundaes, which were carefully and artfully assembled by the flight attendants at her chair as Michaela watched.

Lindsay looked over at Michaela and Kai, and said, "I could get used to this! I don't think I have ever been pampered to this level before!"

Kai replied, "Well, enjoy it! We may be in coach next year, so squeeze every memory out of this that you can."

Wow! Did I just commit to coming again next year? Did I just assume that Lindsay would want to come too?

Kai's thoughts were interrupted by Michaela.

"Mom, do you think we will keep coming?"

"Would you like that?"

"I would."

Lindsay spoke up and said, "I know I would! That is, if you're inviting me."

Kai smiled and said, "I would too. We will have to see what we can do to make that happen."

Uh oh! Now it's time to put up or shut up!

Later in the evening, the lights were dimmed and everyone began to settle in for some rest. Kai looked over at Michaela.

Sleeping again. My little angel.

Kai, on the other hand, was a bit restless and couldn't sleep. A flight attendant noticed and came to her seat.

"Can I get you anything? Maybe a glass of wine? Or some hot chocolate?"

"You know, a glass of wine would be great. I think I remember a Napa Valley Cabernet Sauvignon on the wine list. Do you have any of that one left?"

"Yes, we do. I'll be right back."

The flight attendant returned with a glass, placed a cocktail napkin on Kai's tray, and began to set the wine down just as the plane hit a little turbulence. The wine glass swayed with the plane, but the flight attendant was able to keep from losing even a single drop.

"I'm impressed! I think I would have spilled that all over both of us!"

The flight attendant laughed.

"This is not my first rodeo," she said with a smile.

"Spoken like a true Texan," said Kai. "Is Texas your home?"

"Yes ma'am. Lived in McKinney since the day I was born. You?"

"I'm not from Texas, originally."

The flight attendant smiled and said, "Well, nobody is perfect."

Kai laughed. "I've lived in Denton since I was a senior in high school. I love everything about Texas, with the possible exception that I don't think we really get four seasons like you'll find in other parts of the country."

The flight attendant replied, "Sure we get four seasons. We get summer. We get 'almost summer.' We get 'still summer.' And then we get Christmas!"

"True!" Kai said with a laugh. "And Christmas day is usually very comfortable!"

As the flight attendant went back to her duties, Kai thought about what just happened.

Kai remembered how Michael was great at meeting people. He could strike up conversations with anyone about anything. He didn't have any business goal in mind when he did. He just loved people and loved learning about them. Of course, that particular skillset was very helpful in business as he attracted new clients.

He would often be quite funny in how he would start a conversation with a stranger.

Kai recalled how Michael began a conversation with a particular stranger in the lobby before a performance of Cirque du Soleil in Las Vegas. He noticed a man standing beside them as he and Kai were in line for a glass of wine. Michael looked at the man and gave him a puzzled look. He then pointed at the man and said, "Excuse me." Then after a couple of seconds, he asked, "Do you know me?"

Michael knew that the two men didn't know each other. He just liked to be playful with people.

Kai started laughing as the man said with a bewildered look, "I don't think so… maybe?"

The two men talked and laughed until it was time to take their seats.

I did pretty well just then with the flight attendant. Michael would be proud. Maybe being in sales will come a little more natural to me than I thought.

As she enjoyed some pleasant memories, she remembered Belle's comments about finding something that she truly believed made people's lives better when they owned it. Something that would make Kai feel good about her role as the person who helped them make the connection. Something she could get excited about.

Those thoughts gave Kai quite a bit of comfort. If that was what being in sales was all about, she could see herself doing the job.

She took her last sip of wine.

Hmmm.

I like wine. I'm not sure that it qualifies as improving lives. But it certainly improves my personal outlook on life. And I do get excited about it.

I wonder if there is a way to make money educating people on wine?

Kai drifted off to sleep… as visions of wine corks danced in her head.

Upon arriving in Dallas, the three ladies made the trek from the gate to baggage claim. Then, after retrieving their luggage from the carousel and carrying everything out to the curb, they were pleased to see Kai's parents driving up to meet them.

They were sleepy. They were exhausted. And they were a little sad to not be in Hawaii anymore.

They were also very glad to be back home.

Kai's father, Allen, pulled up to the curb and parked his SUV. He turned on the flashers and got out to help put the bags in the car.

"Hello! How's my favorite granddaughter doing?"

Michaela replied, "Granddad! I'm your only granddaughter! Of course I'm your favorite! There's literally no competition!"

Allen pulled Michaela close and gave her a big bear hug and a kiss on the top of her head.

"Well, even if there was competition, you'd still be my favorite! Or, at least in the top ten!" he said with a wink.

"How are you, Mr. Stephens?" asked Lindsay.

"Doing well, thank you, ma'am! And Lindsay, you are a grown woman now. You are part of the family. I gave you permission to call me Allen years ago."

Allen had been out of the Air Force for quite a while now, but he still kept his hair cut high-and-tight and had an air of leadership that followed him wherever he went.

"I know you did, Mr. Stephens. But I just can't do it."

Kai said, "Well, at least you stopped saluting him. He liked that so much he almost instituted the same policy with me!"

Allen said, "With the whole family, thank you!"

They all laughed as they took their seats in the SUV and left the terminal.

Lindsay turned to Kai's mother and said, "Hi, Kathy. How are you?"

Allen exclaimed, "Hey! Why do you call her by her first name and call me Mr. Stephens?"

Kathy smirked and said, "Because I am sweeter than you!" as everyone laughed.

"That is true. I'll give you that, for sure!"

Kai saw her dad smile at her mother. He had a look of adoration on his face that said more than words could ever convey.

Kathy said, "So tell us about your trip. Did you have fun?"

Michaela was the first to answer.

"We did, Grandma! It was a blast! I got to see where they made the movie *Jurassic Park!*"

"Wow! That does sound fun!"

"And mom met a lady with blue hair who is going to help her get a career… or a business… or something like that going."

"Blue hair?" asked Kathy with surprise.

Kai looked at the rearview mirror and could see her dad's eyes looking back at her. She returned her eyes to her mother, who had quite the quizzical look on her face.

Kai then gave Michaela a glance that only a mother can give… a stare that said, "That will be enough, thank you."

Kai felt awkward. She wasn't sure why. She thought that maybe she was a little concerned about how her dad would respond.

"That's right. I planned to get your thoughts on this later, but I guess now is okay. I met a lady on the beach at Poipu. She has built a very successful business with one of the largest sales teams in the nation. She also coaches and mentors other women who are building careers and businesses. Her name is Belle, and she has offered to mentor me."

"How much does she charge?" asked Allen.

"She has blue hair?" Kathy asked again.

Kai replied, "She's going to mentor me as a friend instead of a client. And yes, Mom, she has blue hair."

"Why?" asked Kathy.

"Well, we just started talking as we had lunch one day. I ended up telling her what we had been through this year, and how I was looking for a way to earn a living now. As we got to know each other, I found that she was a very sharp person with a lot of real-world experience… experience that would come in handy for me right now.

"She offered to mentor me and I accepted her offer."

"No, silly!" replied Kathy. "Why does she have blue hair?"

They all laughed, and Kai told the story of how Belle got her blue hair.

"I've decided I am going into sales," said Kai.

64

Allen asked, "What will you be selling?"

"I don't know yet. I haven't decided."

"Are you sure you want to be in sales?" asked Kathy. "If I remember correctly, you didn't seem to like sales very much on your band fundraisers."

"That was back in high school, Mom. This won't be the same."

Allen said, "Kai, you can really make a lot of money in sales if you pick the right company and product. But you'll have to work very hard. I have no doubt you can learn to do anything. You're also very personable and people love you. I think you'll do well."

Kai thought about what she just heard. She was happy, but also confused.

"Thanks, Dad. I am glad to hear you say that... but I am also a little bit surprised. I didn't expect you to think that me going into sales was a good idea."

"Why not, honey?"

"Because I didn't think you liked salespeople."

"Well, where in the world did you get that idea?"

Allen was truly surprised to hear this.

"I remember you really getting annoyed with that vacuum-cleaner salesman that came to the house when I was in my senior year of high school. And I also think I recall a couple of car salesmen that you wouldn't have wanted to invite to dinner either."

"Oh, honey," Allen replied. "Those were just a couple of idiots who were rude and obnoxious. That doesn't mean that all salespeople are like that."

Allen continued, "Kai, you can't judge a group of people by the actions of a few. I know that you are a grown woman, but apparently, I have been remiss in your education on this particular point… which reminds me of a story."

Kathy interrupted, "Oh no, Allen, not another one of your stories!"

"What do you mean?" asked Allen, with completely faked astonishment, as if he had no idea what Kathy was talking about.

Kai smiled. Michaela giggled.

Over the years, Kai's father had developed quite a reputation as a storyteller. He would often keep a room full of people laughing with a humorous story, on the edge of their seats with a mystery, or simply elicit sighs from the women and stifled tears from the men as he told a story that had a touching life lesson.

This "skill," which he had developed so well, resulted in the fact that the family members may have actually heard the story he was telling before… once… or twice… or a dozen times.

"The girls are tired, and I am sure they don't need to hear one of your stories."

"Now wait just a minute, Kathy. I have a couple of very good reasons that I need to tell this story."

"You *need* to tell this story?" asked Kathy. "Why do you *need* to tell this story?"

"Well, first, there is a significant lesson in this story that Kai, Michaela and Lindsay need to learn. And second, I would kind of like to hear me tell this story again myself. It's one of my favorites, and I like how I tell it!"

As everyone laughed, Allen proceeded with the story as if Kathy had never said a thing.

"Kai, you are going to find that, in this life, there is what I call a 'two-percent horse's…'"

"Allen!" interrupted Kathy. "Your granddaughter is in the car!"

Allen cleared his throat and looked in the mirror at Michaela.

He winked.

She giggled.

He continued, "There will be a 'two-percent horse's… uh… backside' factor in life. Simply put, ninety-eight percent of the people you meet will be just as nice to you as you are to them. They will be friendly. They will be respectful. They will be the type of people that you would enjoy being around."

"However, approximately two percent of the people that you meet will be a complete horse's…"

"Careful…" said Kathy.

"Two percent will be horse's backsides. It doesn't matter how nice you are. It doesn't matter how good you are at what you do. It doesn't matter how hard you try to train them to do their jobs well, two percent will be idiots and jerks, and act like they have no common sense. They will be so snarly and sour that you will think they were breast fed lemon juice and weaned on a pickle!"

Michaela began to laugh, and Lindsay spewed water from her mouth.

"Those 'two percenters' are a pain in the… uh… rear, for sure. But the real trouble comes when we mentally lump them in with the other ninety-eight percent. Sometimes we allow ourselves to expect the ninety-eight percent to behave just like the two percent. And that's not a fair thing to do.

"In society, ninety-eight percent of the people are law-abiding citizens. Two percent aren't. We can't allow ourselves to treat the law-abiding people like the law breakers. It is unfair to them and to us.

67

We would lose something in the process that would keep us from being able to truly enjoy our neighbors.

"Ninety-eight percent of the people of any faith want a peaceful coexistence where you treat other people the same as you want to be treated yourself. Two percent of the people in any faith take things to extremes and do harm. We can't allow ourselves to judge all people by the actions of a few."

Kathy asked, "You just made that two percent number up entirely, didn't you?"

"As a matter of fact, I did," replied Allen. "But I thought it worked quite well, didn't you?"

"I did."

"May I proceed?"

"Yes, you may."

"Thank you."

Kai smiled as she heard the banter go back and forth between her parents. It was a loving and playful exchange that seemed to only come with couples who had shared years together and truly loved each other's company.

Allen continued, "It doesn't matter what grouping society wants to push people into—any time we set our expectations of a whole group, based on the actions of a few people in that group, we do harm to ourselves and to all of humanity.

"And yes, that even applies to salespeople.

"Those salespeople that you mentioned are the exception rather than the rule. Two of my golfing buddies are in sales. They are two of the nicest and most helpful people I know. One of them is Lindsay's dad. They are a credit to their profession. More importantly, they are just good people. The world is better because they are in it.

"So, if you decide to go into sales, be proud of what you do. Do it well. Focus on helping your prospects and customers. Then just go be the best at doing it.

"If you do that, you will be extremely successful."

Lindsay spoke up. "That was motivational, Mr. Stephens! Maybe I want to go into sales now too!"

"I'm glad I can motivate you, Lindsay. I wonder if there might be some way that I could motivate you into calling me Allen?"

Everyone laughed... a tired laugh.

Kathy said, "Alright, Allen. That's enough. Let the ladies sleep for the rest of the ride."

"Okay. I will step down off my bully pulpit... for now."

The car was quiet for the remaining drive. But Kai didn't sleep. She was still thinking about what her dad had said.

She was really glad that he had said it.

After saying their goodbyes, Kai and Michaela checked their mail, unlocked the door, and pulled their suitcases through the front door of their home.

"I think I'm going to take a nap," said Michaela.

Kai replied, "I think I am going to take a long bubble bath... and then take a nap." She glanced down at her phone for the time. "I will wake up in time to make dinner."

"Sounds good," said Michaela, as she yawned, grabbed her bag, and headed into her bedroom.

Kai began to fill her bathtub with hot water and her favorite foaming bath salts. She smiled as she remembered how much Michael loved taking baths.

"I've never heard of a man loving to take baths as much as you," she had remarked on more than one occasion.

"How can I help it after the beautiful bathroom you remodeled for us," she remembered him replying.

Michael's encouragement of her taking on the challenge of remodeling their en suite bathroom had been one of the reasons she decided to do so. When they bought the home, the bathroom had been quite outdated. It had light-blue wallpaper with yellow flowers and red hummingbirds. It had countertops that were covered in white Formica, and faucets that were probably manufactured sometime around the Kennedy assassination.

However, after Kai had completed the remodel, the entire room looked elegant.

There were beautiful wooden cabinets of black cherry, stone countertops with a dazzling mix of colors that Michael had never seen before, and a bathtub that was absolutely stunning. It was an inset tub that had been dropped into a freestanding frame, surrounded in small bronze, black, and red glass tiles.

The tub was also large enough that it would take fifteen minutes just to fill it with water.

Michael had often filled his bath, dropped into the water, and relaxed for an hour as he read a book. Kai had often joined him since there was easily room for two people lounging from opposite ends.

She savored those pleasant memories as she lowered herself into the water and closed her eyes, listening to the music that was playing on the remote speaker she operated from her smart phone.

I miss him so much. But at least it's getting a little easier to enjoy the memories without focusing on the pain.

As she relaxed, she used her phone to go online and search for direct sales opportunities.

She could hear Belle's voice as she scanned the different links that she saw.

"If you want to build a happy life for you and Michaela, the first thing you should remember is that whatever you choose to do in a career or business must match the values you hold most dear."

She thought about her answers that day.

Freedom to be with Michaela when she needs me. Enough income so that money is a non-issue in my life.

Almost as a joke, she decided to type "direct sales wine" into the search bar. To her surprise, there were many listings of sales opportunities that involved hosting wine tastings. Each link led to companies that sold wines, food, and accessories.

I love hosting parties. I love going to parties. And I love wine!

She continued to read until her eyes couldn't stay open any longer. She got out of the tub, dried off, and turned down the bed covers. Yawning, she put on her favorite sleep clothes — one of Michael's blue T-shirts and her white gym shorts, and crawled into the bed for a nice long siesta.

I think that wine sales would be a very good fit.

The sunlight that slipped through the slats of her window blinds grew dimmer and smaller until it had slowly and completely faded into darkness.

Kai was awakened by Michaela crawling into bed with her and slipping under her arm. Noticing the time and realizing that she had slept longer than planned, Kai asked, "Are you hungry?"

"Not really."

"Me either. Want to just sleep on through until breakfast?"

Michaela nodded her head.

"Read me a story?"

Kai smiled. "Sure."

She reached over and turned on the lamp on her nightstand. Then she opened the drawer and pulled out a book that she had been reading to Michaela before they left for Hawaii: *Under A Tree Filled With Birds — And Other Places You Should Never Stand.*

This was one of their favorite books. They loved the title and the story. It was a great parable that helped "tweenagers" understand the value of making good decisions.

As she read to Michaela, the child soon began to snore softly.

I wonder how many more times she will still want me to read to her?

She didn't know the answer. But she did know that one day it would stop. So Kai gazed at her daughter, kissed her softly on the temple, and added this scene to the mental movie that was her life.

6

Kai's body clock was still slightly off-kilter due to the time difference between Texas and Hawaii.

Usually, the natural rhythm of the sun rising each morning would begin the process of waking her. But today, she didn't move a muscle until the sky was bright and Michaela's arm landed across her face.

Gently moving her daughter's arm and trying not to wake her, she slipped out of bed, wiggled her toes on the carpet and walked into the kitchen to start the coffee.

I can't believe I slept until 8:00!

She straightened up the kitchen a bit. Not that there was any real need to do so. It was just her habit to walk around looking for things that needed her attention as she waited on her coffee.

The kitchen table was large, round, and made of solid oak. It was surrounded by two brown leather banquettes and two leather chairs with lush red-and-gold fabric backs. It had what had formerly been a beautiful flower arrangement of Gerbera daisies in the center. However, their lack of water over the course of the last week had taken its toll.

Kai, not ready to give up on them, poured a half-full pitcher of water into the vase.

The coffee maker beeped. She poured herself a cup, grabbed her laptop from the corner of the room, and opened it on the table. She turned it on and slid onto one of the banquettes.

First things first.

One of the few morning rituals that Kai had were the steps she almost ceremonially followed to enjoy her coffee.

She held her cup in both hands, closed her eyes, and brought the cup to her face.

Slowly, she inhaled the aroma. For just a few seconds, she allowed the scent to wrap around her, and it always brought a faint smile to her face. Then with her eyes still closed, she would take the first sip. She would hold it in her mouth and allow the flavor to engulf her taste buds.

Swallowing the coffee was important. But it was only one part of truly enjoying the experience… and Kai wasn't even sure it was her favorite part.

Of course, it was almost always Kona coffee. It was always black. She was never one to put cream or sugar in her coffee. As she thought about it, she remembered that her father drank his coffee the same way. She considered the simple fact that they both liked their coffee black as one of their special bonds.

Okay. Now I'm ready.

She opened her email program and began to compose a message to Belle. The time difference between Texas and Hawaii during this time of year was four hours. Thus Kai knew that it would only be 4:30 a.m. there, and Belle would most likely not be checking her email. But she wanted to make sure that the message would be waiting on her as soon as she woke up.

Good Morning!
We are safely back in Texas and catching up on some sleep. But I was excited and wanted to let you know the direction I think I want to go.

I have always enjoyed wine… well, not always… but always as an adult (as far as my parents know)… LOL! I also have loved to host parties and help my friends plan their gatherings as well.

On the flight back from Honolulu, I began to wonder if there would be some way that I could turn those two loves into a business. When I got home and looked online, I found several direct sales companies that specialize in wines, food and assorted accessories.

I think that would be perfect for me. It would give me the flexibility to be the mother I want to be. It would be doing something I love. And I think it would bring in a good income.

I would love to get your thoughts and ideas
about how to pick a company. When could
we have our first call?

I want you to know how much I really
appreciate your willingness to help me. It is
one of the most kind and thoughtful things
anyone has ever done for me.

Talk to you soon.

Kai

She clicked "send," and sat back for a couple of minutes, closing
her eyes again as she sipped her coffee.

When she reopened her eyes, she noticed someone she assumed to
be her new neighbor carrying boxes into the house across the street
and over one lot.

Someone is moving into the Markham's place.

Kai had been sad to hear that the Markhams were leaving.
Michaela had been heartbroken by the news. Their daughter, Naomi,
and Michaela had been best friends since they were toddlers. They
learned to ride their bikes together on the street in front of their houses.
Down to the cul-de-sac they would pedal, make the curve, and return
to the driveway. They both looked so cute on their bicycles, with
training wheels attached, pink helmets, and matching knee pads.

They rode without smiles and stared intently on the road ahead. Their serious and focused faces showed their determination to successfully complete their course without falling down and skinning their knees.

Naomi's brother, Jude, would often visit as well. It wasn't at all unusual to see the little tyke get dressed in a suit and tie, hop into his battery-operated car, which held exactly two toddlers, and drive over to ask Michaela if she would like to go for a ride. She would accept, and the two would ride around in his car—staring straight ahead— saying not a word.

Just adorable.

Although Michaela didn't want to talk about it, Kai was sure that having her best friend move away just a few months after her dad died was compounding her feelings of loss.

"You will still be able to see each other," Kai had said. "I'll take you over there. It isn't that far away."

Sometimes I really don't know what to do to help her process all of this.

As Kai continued to drink her coffee and watch the new neighbor, Michaela walked into the kitchen.

"Someone new is moving into Naomi's house."

Michaela said nothing, but joined her mother at the table and looked out the window.

"I wonder if they'll have any children."

Michaela still said nothing. Instead, she gave a three-note melodic grunt, which her mother knew meant, "I don't know."

"Hungry?"

Michaela nodded her head and said, "I'll grab some cereal."

"I'll check the milk to see if it's still drinkable," Kai said, opening the refrigerator.

Kai jerked her head back from the opening of the milk carton. "Whoa! That's not going to work! Let's see. Hmm. How about some strawberries and yogurt this morning?"

Again Michaela nodded, returning to the table and looking out the window.

Michaela said, "I don't see anyone else over there with him. No kids. No wife."

Kai sat Michaela's breakfast on the placemat.

"Time will tell. You start back in school on Monday. Is there anything you need to be doing to get ready?"

"Thanks for the reminder, Mom," said Michaela, as she turned and stared at Kai.

The look on her face and the deadpan tone of voice she used made it clear that, although she had thanked her mother, genuine appreciation for the reminder was not the intent of her comment.

Deciding to be a little playful, Kai said in a bright and upbeat tone, "You're welcome, honey! It always makes me happy when you appreciate the little things I do to make your life better!"

Michaela looked at her mother's smile in disbelief, but after a few seconds she shook her head and smiled too.

"I do have a couple of homework assignments that have to be done before Monday."

"I've got some things to do myself. I think we will hang around the house today and maybe have a 'pizza and a movie' night."

After eating breakfast, Michaela went to her room and began getting ready for the day. Kai returned to her laptop and continued her search for direct sales companies in the wine industry.

Wow! There are a lot of options. How do I decide which one is right for me?

She spent a couple of hours reading the information she found online. There were companies that sold only wine. There were others that sold wine and food. Some also sold accessories that every wine enthusiast should have. Corkscrews, carafes, aerators, glasses, chillers, and numerous other items. Some even sold cheese boards and decor you might want to have if hosting a wine tasting at your home.

The common thread seemed to be that the items were sold at in-home parties and you could eventually recruit and train your own sales team.

As Kai continued to read, her email alert sounded, and a message from Belle arrived in her inbox.

Good Morning, Kai!

I'm glad you made it home safely. I am also super-excited that you may have found the direction you want to go. And it's my pleasure to be a help to you in any way I can.

Want to jump on our first call right now?

Belle

A link was at the bottom of the email, giving Kai access to Belle's online-meeting platform.

I don't even have on any makeup!

"Oh, what the heck! Let's do this!" Kai said as she clicked the link.

A couple of minutes later, the two ladies were face to face online and ready to begin.

"Oh, I love your kitchen, Kai! It's beautiful!"

"Thank you!" she replied as she rotated her laptop so that Belle could see the full 360-degree view.

"Did you do that yourself?"

"Yes, I did! It's a combination of rag-rolling and sponging three different paint colors."

"It's gorgeous!"

"Well, thank you. But it pales in comparison to the way you have decorated your office!"

Belle laughed and turned her laptop around giving Kai the full 360-degree view of Poipu beach.

"I'm jealous!"

"The decor is great — but the best part is my rent! I like reasonable and low cost, but free is definitely my favorite price! And I don't have to pay a thing to office here. Granted, Hawaii is an expensive place to live overall. But I wouldn't trade this for any other place on earth."

After a couple of minutes of small talk, Belle began.

"So, I am excited about your idea of going into the wine-sales industry. You know, I have a cousin back in Georgia who is in the alcohol-sales industry."

"Really?" asked Kai.

"Yes. Well, he doesn't call it sales. He calls it 'bootlegging!'"

Laughing, Kai said, "You say potāto, I say potáto. Alcohol sales… bootlegging."

"Not sure if you have ever watched a NASCAR race before, but bootlegging is what gave birth to that sport," said Belle.

"Fast-running cars would have been handy back then. Makes sense to me. I like to drive fast! Maybe I would have been good at that!" replied Kai, laughing.

Belle continued, "So tell me what you've been finding."

"It seems that there are several companies that have similar business models. They sell a variety of wines, accessories, foods, and other items that would complement a wine tasting. They all seem to use in-home parties to sell the products and recruit new people."

"That's pretty standard," said Belle.

"The thing is, Belle, they all look great. The product and plan make sense to me. Their websites are all fantastic. Quite frankly, I have no idea how to choose one of them for myself. Do you have any suggestions?"

Belle considered Kai's question, nodded her head, and began to mentor.

"I do have a couple of thoughts. But before I talk about that, let me ask you something. How do each of them align with your values?

Will they allow you to build the life that you want, without sacrificing the things you hold most dear?"

"I think so," replied Kai. "But at this stage, I am not sure that I know everything that will be involved. There will be evening parties. So I need to make sure that I can balance my time properly and ensure that Michaela and I have plenty of time together."

Belle said, "We will talk more about that later as you get to that stage. I will give you some of the same suggestions that I give the mothers on my team. The main thing to remember is to involve Michaela in the business. Make it an 'us' thing rather than a 'me' thing. Once you are comfortable that building your wine business will align with your values, then you can start looking for the right company to choose."

"I'm listening."

"The first thing I recommend looking for is a well-established company that has a good history in the industry. I'd look at their track record. Who are the owners? Is it a public company or private company? What is the background story and does it fit with your values? Going with a start-up company isn't necessarily where I would look. That being said, there can always be exceptions to any generalization, and companies that are well established today were once start-ups."

"Makes sense to me," said Kai.

"I would also do an online search about the company. Look for reviews and lawsuits to see what you find."

"Lawsuits?"

"Yes. Most large companies in any industry will have them. I wouldn't be overly concerned about lawsuits unless I saw numerous class action lawsuits brought by distributors, or any type of governmental interventions toward them."

"Oh. Okay."

"Also, don't be too concerned if you see some negative reviews. I've been doing this long enough to know that most of the negative comments that you see online regarding any direct sales company are from people who thought they would begin a new career and immediately generate large incomes. Then, when they found out that becoming successful is more of a marathon than a sprint and it takes a lot of hard work, they became disgruntled and wanted to blame someone else for their results. But the real culprit was their lack of consistent effort."

"Okay. I am mentally prepared for that, I think. Not everyone will become a customer and no one is going to build my business for me. But if I keep after it, I can build something great for Michaela and myself."

"Funny that you should say that. It brings up another one of my rules for you," said Belle.

"What rule is that?"

"Rule number three: *The Consistency Rule.* You can't control a lot of things, but you can control how consistent you are.

"You can't control whether people say 'yes' or 'no' to buying wine from you. But you *can* be consistent in asking if they would like to buy. You can't control how many others will want to join your team. But you *can* be consistent in making the opportunity available to them. You can't control the various things that life will often send your way. But you *can* be consistent in how you respond with a great attitude, a careful plan and an expectancy that you can find good things from most situations. Even tough situations can teach valuable lessons.

"You can't control the choices made by others… but you *can* control the choices made by you."

"What do you mean?" asked Kai.

"You can *choose* to control your motivation. You have to find your 'why'. For you, of course, that is probably the life you want to build for you and Michaela. Keep reminders around that fill your heart with that beautiful little girl."

Belle continued, "You can *choose* to control your skillset. Put in the work to get really great at what you do. Ask the right questions to find out what your prospect really desires. Help them find it. Guide them through the steps so that they can own what they want. When you've done your job well, and helped make an easy connection between your company and your prospect, many will become your customers. But if they don't, allow yourself to detach from their choice, knowing that you did a great job, and they did or didn't buy based upon their own reasons."

"Okay," said Kai.

"Next, you can *choose* to have a positive mental attitude. That takes work, but it is worth doing. A positive attitude will not guarantee your success. But a negative attitude will almost certainly guarantee your failure.

"Finally, you can *choose* to control your activity level. That's the multiplier for everything. Your motivation, skills and attitude are extremely important. But your activity level is the final determining factor. You can be highly motivated, have a great attitude, and be an absolute expert at what you do, but if your activity level is zero…"

Kai interrupted, "I remember this from algebra class. Anything multiplied by zero is going to be zero."

Belle laughed and said, "That's right! You get an 'A'! So if you are a highly motivated expert with no activity — you will be a highly motivated expert who is flat broke! But if you are highly motivated and skillful, and you have a great attitude with consistently high activity levels, you will do very well indeed."

"I can't control a lot of things, but I *can* control how consistent I am."

"That's right!"

"Are there any other things I should look for when picking a company?"

Belle replied, "Yes. I have a couple of other suggestions for you."

"I would look for companies that are a member of the Direct Selling Association or the Direct Selling World Alliance. You can check out both of their websites: www.dsa.org and www.dswa.org to find out more. Companies that are members of those organizations tend to have more credibility in my eyes and in the industry.

"Finally, you want to get in with a really great upline."

"What's an upline?" Kai asked.

Belle replied, "Your upline is a term for the people who are your leaders in your sales team. They help get you going and support you. For that, they make a small override on your sales. You always make the most money from your efforts. And they make a little bit for what they do to help you. That's one of the most important factors that can help you succeed. When a strong upline is there for you, you'll have a place to get the training and support you'll need.

"When you've narrowed your search to a couple of companies, let me know and I will reach out to my contacts and try to help you find a great upline. I am a member of the DSWA, and I may be able to make the right connections for you."

"I will," said Kai. "You haven't said anything about compensation. What do you look for there?"

"Compensation is important, and I look at that. But it's not the most important in my opinion. The background story and how a company treats its distributors is what matters most to me."

"Okay. I have some things to work with now. Thank you, Belle!"

"My pleasure! One final rule for today, and then I have to run.

"Rule number four is *The Wood Stove Rule:* You have to put wood in the stove first before it will ever provide heat for you.

"Have you ever used a wood stove to heat your home?"

Kai replied, "No. I've seen them but I have never used one."

"I used one for years until I moved to Kauai. I loved the ambience they brought to my home, and they put out a surprising amount of heat.

"The way a wood stove works is that you put wood into the firebox first, then light the fire. Once you have done that, the stove radiates heat throughout your home."

"Okay. Where are you going with this one?" Kai asked with a smile.

"I'm glad you asked," replied Belle, as she smiled in return. "Treat your business like a wood stove. Be willing to feed it first—and then it will provide for you. You will need to invest in your business."

Kai asked, "What type of investing are you referring to? Things like inventory or office space?"

"No. With technology today, most direct sales companies can move their products out so quickly that inventory is not a requirement. Some companies even recommend against keeping inventory of your own. Also, in the beginning at least, you should office at home and keep your expenses low.

"I'm talking about investing in your personal growth through books and podcasts that build your self-image, sales skills, and business acumen. You will also want to take advantage of training meetings put on by the company or your upline. That is all part of getting good at what you do. It will also help you maintain a great attitude.

"You'll also need to invest in marketing supplies such as brochures and advertising. You may eventually want to hold your own training meetings and have rewards for your salespeople or take them to lunch occasionally. I always send out cards to team members and customers for birthdays and just to say thank you. I actually use an online service for that. With all of those things, your goal is to build wonderful and long-lasting relationships.

"I've seen people who seemed to approach their business with the wrong mindset. They weren't willing to invest in any of these things until they were making enough money from their business to cover their costs. That would be like standing in front of a wood stove and saying, give me heat first... then I will give you wood."

"I see your point," said Kai. "Investing first is just good common business sense."

"True. But, as in many areas of life today, common sense is unfortunately not all that common."

Kai said, "I remember the early days of Michael's business. We lived quite frugally and invested in his business. He needed an office, office supplies and even an employee. He also advertised and attended various functions. Eventually, the business became successful and we reaped the benefit."

"You put the wood in the stove, and it eventually gave your family heat."

"That's right."

Belle continued, "I think you'll find that the investment you will be making in your wine business will be much less than what you and Michael had to do."

"Alright," said Kai. "I'll do some more research and let you know where that leads. Is there anything else I need to be doing?"

"Yes. Go give Michaela a hug and a kiss from me. Let's talk again next week," said Belle.

"That sounds good. Thank you again, Belle. I am truly grateful for your help."

"My pleasure!"

With that, the two ladies finished their call. Kai closed her laptop, poured another cup of coffee, and walked down the hall into Michaela's room.

Kai gave her daughter a hug and a kiss.

"That's from Belle," Kai told her.

Michaela said, "I need to meet her. Maybe I can say hi on your next call."

"Oh, I should've thought to do that today, sweetie! I'm sorry. We will make sure to do that next week. Are you through with your homework?"

"Not yet," replied Michaela.

"Me either. See you in a few hours. Then we will order that pizza."

As Kai turned to walk back to the kitchen, Michaela said, "I love you, Mom."

Kai turned back and looked at her daughter and smiled… her heart melted into a sweet and sticky puddle of goo.

"Oh… I love you too, Michaela. To the moon and back."

7

Wow!

So much had happened over the last three weeks!

Kai made the decision on which company she wanted to work with. After researching the things Belle had mentioned, she selected a company called Special Memories Wine Club. The company's story was truly remarkable. The product line was varied and had pretty much everything Kai would need to host a gathering of friends or family. Even more important to Kai, the company founders had been the subjects of articles she found in two publications that were both very family focused. The articles had been quite flattering, and the husband and wife seemed to be the kind of people Kai would easily invite into her home.

True to her promise, Belle had checked with her contacts with Special Memories Wine Club and had a recommendation for an upline that she believed would provide great support for Kai.

Belle had said, "Tammie Bond has been with Special Memories Wine Club for many years. Her organization has a great reputation for being helpful in training and support. Tammie is also a very nice person. I met her at a function a few years ago. She is funny and kept me in stitches at one of the dinners we attended. I was fortunate to be seated at the same table with her. It was so much fun!"

Kai met with Tammie the next week and found that Belle was exactly correct. The two ladies laughed so much trying to complete Kai's online signup to become a new distributor, that she wondered if they were going to be able to finish the process.

"Kai, go ahead and log into my Wi-Fi on your laptop," said Tammie.

"Okay."

As Kai began the Wi-Fi network search, she found something surprising.

"Wait a minute! This's weird! The only Wi-Fi network I see is called 'CIA Surveillance Van!'"

Kai looked out the window, almost expecting to see a nondescript white van.

Tammie laughed and said, "Oh, that's mine. I have a neighbor who is a bit of a paranoid type and believes everything he reads online. So, I decided to play with him a little. I renamed my Wi-Fi network 'CIA Surveillance Van' just to see what he would do. Literally, within thirty minutes of doing so, I saw him come out of his house, sweeping his eyes up and down the street with a very concerned look on his face."

"You're kidding me!"

"No. I finally went out and talked with him. I said, 'What's up, Marcus?' He looked suspiciously throughout the neighborhood and said, 'Oh… nothing. Have you seen any strange-looking vehicles around lately? In particular, any type if van with the windows blacked out?'

"I said, 'Now that you mention it, I have. I didn't think anything about it at the time. It was a white-paneled van that, other than the windshield and front seats, had no windows at all.'

"Then I said, 'Why do you ask?' He ignored my question and asked, 'Where was it?'

"I said, 'Parked right across from your driveway.'"

Kai exclaimed, "You're terrible! That poor man!"

"Oh, he's fine! He went back inside. I didn't see him come out for several days. Though I did see his curtains move a few times!" Tammie said, laughing.

As they visited, Kai was glad to hear Tammie mention some of the same things in her training that Belle had also mentioned on their call. There would be no need to stock inventory, other than what she wanted to use for an actual party she would be leading. However, she should expect to invest in advertising materials, training meetings and her personal growth.

"Do you have any book recommendations for me to get started with?" Kai asked.

"Yes, I do. My first recommendation is to buy *The Go-Giver: A Little Story About a Powerful Business Idea.* It is co-authored by Bob Burg and John David Mann. It is an easy-to-read parable that does a great job of teaching us where we should be focused as we build our businesses."

Over the next week, Kai attended two parties with Tammie for training purposes. It was great to see how Tammie handled each meeting. She had obviously done this many times over her years with the company.

I wonder how long it will take me to be as great at this as Tammie.

Kai's job at Tammie's meetings was to simply observe. Of course, she helped with setting everything up and taking it all down after the tasting. But for the most part, she just watched Tammie and made notes as to how she did her job.

One particular thing that Tammie did was unexpected, in Kai's mind.

As she walked around the room, meeting the guests and thanking them for attending, Tammie would ask some great questions just to get to know more about them. Then, when appropriate, she would introduce different guests to each other.

"Nakia, this is Gracen. Gracen is a realtor in the area. Gracen, this is Nakia. She just mentioned to me that she and her husband are looking for a new home near Riverside Park."

When Kai got a moment alone with Tammie, she asked, "I've noticed you introducing people tonight. I am getting the impression that you are not doing that by accident. That's intentional, right?"

"Yes, it is. Nice observation."

"That is actually something I learned in that book I recommended to you, *The Go-Giver*. When I am working… scratch that… not just when I am working… I am pretty much always looking to find ways to connect people when I see a potential way to help both parties.

"I started off thinking I would do so primarily because it would help my business. I also knew that I would be helping the people I met. But I soon found that an unexpected, yet very real, benefit of focusing on helping others connect was how it made me feel. I love it! Yes, I've certainly gained more new customers because of the goodwill and business leads that naturally flow from being a connector like that. But the truth is that it makes me feel great to do it."

Kai said, "Well, you are superb at it! And that all makes perfect sense to me. I will start reading the book tonight."

"There is one other thing I always do during the meeting itself… usually near the end, which I also learned from that book."

"What's that?"

"I'm not going to tell you. CLIFFHANGER!"

Kai laughed.

Tammie said, "Actually, *Ms. Observant*, I want to see if you catch it."

Kai watched the meeting from the back of the room. Tammie threw several questions out to the crowd. Her intent? To hear the stories they would share.

"What's your favorite memory of a gathering in which you shared wine with your guests?"

She listened to a couple of stories from the group.

"What's your most meaningful memory of you and your spouse, or significant other, that involves wine?"

Again, she listened.

"What's your favorite wine? How do you go about getting your wine?"

She asked several other questions. But as she was closing the conversation from her presentation, she asked the question that Kai was sure had to be the one she was referring to earlier.

"I've enjoyed meeting you all this evening. I really appreciate all of you being here. This is how I make my living. It's how I feed my family. So, thank you for being a part of that.

"I would like to return the favor to you. I make a lot of business and personal connections with people out there every day. And I often find that I can refer people to each other in ways that help both of them."

Nakia spoke up. "She did that for Gracen and me tonight! Gracen is going to help me find a house."

Tammie smiled. "I was glad to do it. So, after I wrap this up, please come see me. I would love to know the answer to this specific question."

She paused for a second, then continued.

"What questions do I need to be asking people to know if they would be a great referral to send your way? It can be business, or personal. But please come up and visit with me and tell me what I should ask them. I will do my best to help you make the connections you need."

One lady almost yelled out a question. "Do you know any good-looking single guys with a job and good table manners?"

The crowd broke into laughter.

Maybe it was the wine. Maybe it was the food.

Or maybe it was how genuinely Tammie was focused on wanting to meet everyone and help them in any way she could. But for the next hour, people kept coming up to her and visiting. It was non-stop. Tammie took notes and wrote their contact information down.

After the activities settled down a bit, Kai said, "That was great! I think almost everyone visited with you."

Tammie smiled. "And I will do everything I can to help each in whatever way is appropriate. Most of them also have already started helping me as well. They made purchases for what they wanted, and several committed to having gatherings in their homes too."

"That's amazing!"

Kai said, "At first I thought you asking the group about their favorite stories involving wine was the thing you wanted *Ms. Observant* to spot. But I later decided that it was that question at the end that was the big deal. The one where you asked how you could refer business to them or make connections for them."

"Ding! Ding! Ding! Give the lady a prize! The stories are very important. Details may give the logical reasons as to why buying the wine from our company makes sense. But emotion is what gets the ball rolling and makes them want to buy. Great stories create emotions. I can tell them some of my own if needed. But getting the crowd to share theirs can be powerful."

"That makes sense," said Kai.

"But you're right. The question at the end was what I wanted to see if you noticed. The funny thing, Kai, is that my intent is truly to help them. I follow through. It's become a way of life for me. As a result of having this mindset, everyone wins. And because I am helping them, they naturally seem to want to help me succeed as well."

Kai started her personal-development journey that very night before going to sleep.

"What are you reading, Mom?" asked Michaela, as she snuggled up to her mother.

"It's a book I downloaded tonight. It will help me get better at our business."

"Can I read it too?"

"Absolutely," replied Kai. "I want this to be our business... not just my business. So I think that would be a great idea. But let's wait until tomorrow," said Kai as she turned off the light. "I've got a big day ahead."

A big day indeed. Or, maybe more appropriately, a big night.

Kai was holding her first party. She had asked Lindsay if she would be the host. Of course, her best friend said yes.

"Having a glass of wine… or two… or three… and helping my best friend get her business started? This is an absolute 'no-brainer' for me. I would love to be your first host."

The date had been set for just a few days later… and that day was now here.

Kai had prepared. She had discussed everything with Tammie and believed she was ready. Even so, she was also quite nervous. She hadn't spoken in front of people very often. And although this was just a home gathering with seven people, the "butterflies" Kai felt couldn't have been stronger if she was preparing to walk out on stage in front of hundreds.

Sensing Kai's uneasiness, Lindsay said, "You're going to do great tonight. These are just a few of my work friends. They are all nice people. They will be a perfect first group for you."

Kai wanted Lindsay's words to be comforting. But her "butterflies" continued to flutter.

About thirty minutes before the gathering was scheduled to officially begin, Tammie walked in. She introduced herself to Lindsay, complimented Kai on how she had set up for the party, and then pulled her to the side.

"Are you ready?"

"I think so," replied Kai. "Just a little nervous."

"Don't worry about that. We are all nervous on our first time. I thought I was going to get physically ill. Just be you. Enjoy the time with your friends. And know that I will be hanging out in the back of the room if you need me."

" You've got this, and I've got you."

Kai nodded her head, and began to visit with the guests that were starting to arrive.

When the party was over and the last guest left, Kai sighed with a sense of relief and sat down on Lindsay's sofa.

"Wine, please."

Lindsay said, "Coming right up. Can I get something for you, Tammie?"

She smiled and replied, "I'll have whatever Kai is having."

"Malbec, please."

To say that Kai was exhausted wouldn't be accurate. The physical activity was minimal. However, her body had not informed her brain of such things. So *exhausted* was exactly how she felt.

"Thank you," said Kai, as Lindsay handed her a glass of Malbec.

"Thank you," said Tammie.

"My pleasure."

Tammie looked at Kai.

"So, how do you think it went tonight?"

Kai replied, "I forgot a lot of things because I was nervous. When I visited with everyone before we got started, I was so mentally focused on what I needed to do next that I totally forgot to see if I could make any connections. I also felt like I made the evening last too long.

"During the tasting, I forgot to ask questions and set up the idea of each person coming to see me afterwards. I was also so uncomfortable asking people to buy. One of the girls actually had to ask me, 'Would it be okay if I bought something?'"

The three ladies laughed.

"Overall? I would give myself a 'C' or so."

"I thought you did great!" said Lindsay.

Tammie thought for a few seconds and said, "Kai, you gave yourself a 'C.' I don't see it that way. I saw a woman who had never done anything like this before get up in front of a group people — most of whom she didn't know — and make some magic happen."

"Really?" asked Kai.

"Absolutely! You were nice. You were fun. You gave some great information about the wines and the other items. You also sold some wine! I would give you a solid 'A'!"

"I did sell some wine, didn't I? She had to ask if it was okay to buy! But I filled out the order. So, yes, I sold some wine!" Kai laughed.

Tammie continued. "I am going to give you two pointers for the night, and then I am going to head home. First, it is perfectly okay to let people know you get a little nervous, and then ask them if they mind you using notecards. They will, of course, be fine with that. And your authenticity will often have them quietly cheering for you to do a good job. Plus, it will help you remember things you left out tonight."

"Alright. And second?"

"You will get more comfortable with practice… so, do it again soon."

"Definitely," said Kai. "I already have another tasting booked for Friday."

Tammie left the house, and Lindsay and Kai packed everything up.

"I like her, Kai. She seemed really nice and very supportive."

"I agree. Belle pointed me in her direction. It was a good choice. Belle and I have a call tomorrow at noon. I will let her know that as well."

Kai left for home and got a good night's sleep.

The next day, after taking Michaela to school and running a few errands, Kai headed home to get set up for her call with Belle.

"Good morning!" Kai said.

"Good afternoon to you!" replied Belle. "I can't wait to hear everything about your party last night. How did it go?"

Kai related the events of the evening, replaying everything she could remember down to the last detail… including the fact that her one and only sale was to a lady who had to ask her, "Would it be okay for me to buy something?"

Belle laughed and told Kai, "That's not the worst closing I've ever heard. I had a man on my team who once asked a prospect, 'You wouldn't want to buy this, would you?'"

"I don't feel so bad now after hearing that one!" Kai burst into laughter.

Belle said, "You know, Kai, one of the easiest ways to close any sale is giving a simple choice between two or three great alternatives."

"What do you mean?"

"Instead of asking if they would like to buy anything…"

"Or waiting on them to ask me?" Kai asked with a laugh.

Belle laughed.

"Just ask them, 'Would you like for me to help you get some reds, some whites or both tonight?' Don't complicate it. Don't draw it out. Just help them get what they need."

"I can do that."

"Also, let me ask you a question. When you think about the things you love best about wine and hosting parties, what comes to mind? Why do you like it so much?"

"Oh, that's easy. It's spending time with my friends and my family."

"How does that make you feel?"

"It's my favorite feeling, after time with Michaela. It makes me feel the warmth of belonging to those around me — and them belonging to me."

"Perfect!" said Belle. "It's your favorite feeling after your time with Michaela. So, when you are closing the sale, you aren't asking them to buy something they may or may not need. You are asking them if they would like you to help them enjoy the sense of warmth they get from belonging with their friends and family. And you are asking them so that you can spend more time with Michaela. You will never hesitate to help them own your products if that is how you see your job."

Kai agreed.

"I have an assignment for you. Get an index card, and write something on it like what you just told me: 'I'm helping people enjoy the warmth of belonging with their family and friends so that I can spend more time with my baby girl.' Attach it to a picture of Michaela. Then take a look at it just before starting every meeting."

"I like that idea," replied Kai.

"Work on your conversations. Get great at what you do. Make notes of the questions you want to ask. Keep your focus on the value you bring to those people who come to the gatherings. If you do those things, nothing will be able to keep you from succeeding."

Kai nodded in agreement.

"You mentioned that you felt like your meeting ran a little long."

"That's right."

"That makes this the perfect time to teach you rule number five!"

Kai was having so much fun learning the rules now. She said, "Give it to me!"

"Rule number five is *The Miniskirt Rule.*"

"The Miniskirt Rule?" asked Kai, laughing with surprise.

"That's right! *The Miniskirt Rule!* Think of your presentations like your miniskirt. Keep them short enough to hold everyone's attention. But long enough to cover the goods!"

Kai laughed so hard, she almost couldn't catch her breath. Belle joined her.

When the laughter finally died down, Belle's tone turned a little serious.

"One last thing I want to tell you before we get off the call today."

"Alright," said Kai, noting the change in Belle's face.

"When you were telling me about the gathering, your focus was on what you did wrong. And to a certain extent, that's okay. We have to know what we need to do better… if we are ever going to actually do it better. And by the way, Tammie's advice to you was spot on. I knew I liked that girl."

"I like her too. She was a great choice for me, Belle. Thank you."

"My pleasure," said Belle. "But I want you to promise me something."

"Anything."

"I want you to only spend a little time on what you think you did wrong… and then spend ten times that amount of time on what you did well. I want you to find something you feel good about in everything you do. It may be from societal norms. It may be from our own introspection. For some, it can even be from toxic relationships where our partners or parents were too critical and not supportive. But we women, all too often, tend to see our shortcomings, real or imagined, and not our strengths.

"We can be quick to see our flaws and slow to see our beauty."

Kai thought for a few seconds, then replied, "Fortunately for me, I was raised by wonderful loving parents who have always believed in me. And my husband was amazingly supportive in his words and his actions. So that wasn't an issue. But I see what you mean, and I promise that I will take it to heart and do what you asked."

There was silence on the computer for a moment. The look in Belle's eyes gave Kai the feeling that she wasn't just talking from things she had read. Instead, maybe she was mentoring Kai from things that had touched her heart personally in some way.

"Kai, you are a wonderful mother and a strong and beautiful woman. You are intelligent. And I have no doubt that you can succeed at this or any other thing you set your mind upon. This is going to be so much fun watching you soar!"

"Thank you, Belle. I appreciate you so much. Same time next week?"

"Yes ma'am! Give Michaela a hug and kiss from me."

"Will do."

And with that, the two women closed their laptops and went on with their day.

8

Snowstorms in the Dallas-Fort Worth area are about as frequent as the number of times that a politician campaigns on the platform of "term-limits," and then holds to that same position after getting elected.

Can it happen? Sure.

Does it happen? Not very often.

Kai remembered Michael saying that politics *used to* keep him quite annoyed. But finally, after studying the linguistics of the word "politics," his frustration became less of an issue.

Michael would say, "The word *politics* is made up of two root words: *poly,* which means 'many,' and *ticks,* which are 'blood-sucking parasites'! Understanding the genesis of the word seems to help it all make sense to me. They can't help being who they are. But we would certainly be better off without so many of them."

During the first week of March, one of those rare and unexpected "snowstorms" had indeed blanketed the Dallas-Fort Worth area with a traffic-snarling, school-closing, four inches of fresh white powder.

105

One of Kai's friends from college, Bernadette, had called to tease her about how North Texans behave during even the slightest of snows.

"Schools and businesses don't close here in Connecticut unless we're having blizzard conditions and it's 'Let Your Toddler Drive to Work Day'!"

Kai laughed and said, "Don't worry about us, Bernadette. We will rebuild!"

Michaela, like most kids her age, loved snow days. She and her dad used to carry a thermos filled with hot chocolate and cinnamon out onto the front porch. Sips of cocoa, along with the careful construction of a snow family consisting of a mom, dad, and daughter were the only things on their agenda. The two would inevitably get into a snowball fight and lure Kai out into the mix.

Today, however, Michaela had no interest in going outside and joining the neighborhood kids as they took advantage of the time off from school. Instead, she had cuddled up on the sofa with a blanket and was playing a game on her phone.

"Would you like to go out and build a snowman together?" Kai asked, fearing that Michaela would just view it as reminder that her dad was no longer here.

Who am I kidding? She always knows Michael's not here. So do I. Reminder or not, we always remember.

"No thanks."

Michaela didn't even look up from her game when she replied.

Kai had noticed a change in Michaela as of late. She was less talkative. She didn't seem to have much interest in the usual things she loved to do, such as riding her bicycle, talking with her friends, or going to the movies. And on her last math test, a subject in which she normally aced exams without even having to study, Michaela received an unusually low score.

One of her teachers, Mrs. Poplin, even sent a note home to Kai asking how things were going.

Even though she knew that the grieving process took a tremendous amount of time, and was different for every person, Kai couldn't help but wonder if there was more going on with Michaela. She walked over to the sofa and wrapped her arms around her little girl... who wasn't so little anymore, and gave her a kiss on the cheek.

"Can I ask you a question?"

Michaela looked at her mother, raised an eyebrow and said, "Mom. It's *may* I ask you a question?"

Both laughed at the role reversal they had just witnessed.

Kai smiled and asked, "Okay. *May* I ask you a question?"

"Sure."

How am I going to approach this in a way that gets her to open up and talk to me?

Kai thought for a few seconds and said, "I feel like I'm really struggling right now. I'm missing your dad. I'm trying to get used to a new career. I'm missing you when we aren't together. I don't feel as interested in things as I used to be. I don't feel quite like myself. I don't know. I guess I'm just feeling kind of down lately."

Kai sighed. "Is the same thing happening to you?"

Michaela didn't say anything. She just looked at her mom, fought back her tears, and nodded her head.

Kai asked, "Do you think you could talk to me about what you're feeling? I think it would help me with my feelings too."

With that, Michaela's tears could no longer be held back.

She sobbed.

"Nothing is the same! I'm missing dad and it hurts! You used to be here from the time I got home from school 'til bedtime! Now you're gone a lot! I'm with the babysitter a lot! And I just want to cry a lot!"

Now it was Kai trying to hold back the tears.

But as the first drop ran down her cheek, she decided that it was probably best that Michaela see that she too was hurting. She could still be strong for her daughter, while also showing her true emotions as well. In fact, allowing those emotions to flow would probably be good for them both.

"I get it, baby. Nothing's the same anymore. And our interest in doing the things we used to love... well... those things don't appeal to us so much nowadays. The man we loved doing them with isn't here to do them with us."

She squeezed Michaela a little tighter.

"Your dad being gone really sucks!"

Michaela was a little surprised at her mom's unusual choice of words. Through her tears, with a bit of a laugh and with a slightly running nose, she said, "You said 'sucks'! And you're right. That's exactly what it does. It sucks!"

"I think we both have to remember that your dad being gone is just going to make our lives different. Things won't be as we expected. That difference makes us sad. It makes us a little scared too. But we can still have a happy life. We just have to find ways to make that happen. Your dad loved us, and making a happy life is exactly what he'd want us to do.

Kai continued, "I think if we are always talking with each other about what's going on inside us… what we're feeling… that will help. I know it'll help me."

"Me too," said Michaela, wiping her face with a tissue.

"How do you think we should go about doing that?" asked Kai.

"Mom, one thing for me is that I don't want be away from you so much."

"I don't want that either, baby. I'll get some advice from Belle. She had mentioned a couple of things a while back about how to make sure that you and I were in this new business together. But I don't think I've been doing a very good job on that. I apologize."

"Apology accepted."

"We will find a solution to that together. It won't just be me. You will help me make the decisions. Does that sound good to you?"

"Yes ma'am."

"Now I need something from you too."

"What?"

"I need to go out and build a snowman! Are you in?"

Michaela smiled and said, "I am! Can we make hot chocolate?"

"Yes!"

"With cinnamon?"

"I wouldn't have it any other way."

The two ladies hurried to make the cocoa, get their coats and gloves on, and then raced out the door.

As they built the snowman and tossed a few snowballs around, Michaela noticed the new neighbor across the street.

He waved.

Michaela waved back.

Kai turned to see that it was the same man who had been moving boxes into the house where the Markhams had lived. He waved at Kai as well. She smiled, a little too awkwardly, and gave a half wave back in his direction.

As Kai and Michaela continued in their winter fun, Michaela said, "Mom, I think that guy was checking you out."

"I'm sure he wasn't. I don't want him to," said Kai. She was uncomfortable with even the thought of that right now. Occasionally, she considered that she might date again someday. But today was definitely not "someday."

By Saturday morning, the Texas weather did what the Texas weather does.

It drastically changed... and it did so rather quickly.

The winter-weather scene from only two days prior had melted away. In its place was an absolutely gorgeous day that would have made a great photo for any magazine advertising, "Come to north Texas!" The temperature was a comfortable seventy-three degrees, an easy breeze was blowing from the north, and Kai had opened every window in the house to enjoy it.

Kai opened her laptop and clicked on the link for her scheduled meeting with Belle.

"Good morning! How are things in beautiful Poipu this morning?"

"Absolutely amazing, as usual! I really am spoiled, you know?"

Kai laughed.

"That reminds me of a Michael story! When Michaela was a baby, Michael would hold her so much that my parents would say, 'You're spoiling that child.' He would then lay her on his shoulder, pull her diaper out a little bit from behind and sniff. Then with a sour look on his face, he would say, 'She's not spoiled. She just smells that way!'"

The two ladies laughed.

"It made the news out here that the Dallas area got an unusual snowstorm. Is everything okay?"

Kai laughed and said, "Yes it is. As a matter of fact it is a beautiful pre-spring day today." She turned her laptop around so that Belle could see as well.

Michaela rounded the corner, stuck her head into the camera view and said, "Hi, Belle!"

"Well hello there, young lady! How are you?"

"I'm fine thanks!"

"So what does a busy young lady like you have planned for such a nice day?"

"I was thinking I would ride my bike over to my friend Gemma's house."

Turning to her mother, she asked, "Mom. Is it okay if I go to Gemma's?"

"Have you called and asked her mom if it would be alright?"

"Yes. She said it's fine."

"Okay. Text me when you get there."

"Will do. Bye, Belle!"

And as quickly as she came into view, Michaela was gone again.

"She just seems like such a joy!"

Kai replied, "She is. And speaking of Michaela, I have a couple of questions for you."

"Okay, go ahead," said Belle.

Kai recounted the conversation she and Michaela had before going out to build a snowman.

"You had mentioned that you would have some recommendations for me in this area. Please share them. I'm already having her do things with me that have to be done on a day-to-day basis. But I want to do more. She's really missing me in the evening. I plan to include Michaela in finding the solution, but I would love to have some direction from you as to how I can involve her more in our business."

"Sure. I'll be happy to."

"First, let me say that you are already going in the right direction when you refer to your new career as 'our business.' I've heard many people describe their new endeavor as 'my business' or 'the business.' It's my opinion that those phrases are a mistake for parents. Including your children in as many ways as possible is much better. Giving them ownership — even if it's only in your words — makes them feel like an important part of the picture.

"In any business, there'll be times when extra work will be needed. When that happens, just the simple step of calling it 'our business' can help to soothe any bad feelings that may rise to the surface."

Belle asked, "Do you think the main issue is Michaela missing you in the evenings when you're doing your tastings?"

"I think so."

"The quick answer is to take her with you when appropriate. Granted, balancing the needs of a child with schoolwork, eating and getting enough rest have to come first. But it's often quite easy to take her with you and have her help with set up and take down. She could do her homework. You may even have her babysit when your host has small children."

"That's a great idea. I had a tasting last week, and the host's children were quite a distraction."

"If Michaela were going to be a distraction, I would advise you not to do so. But she is such a mature kid for her age, I don't think that will be an issue. Start small. Maybe you start off trying it only for one evening per week. If that goes well, you can increase it to two… then three. If it starts to affect Michaela negatively, you can always back things down a night or two. If there are no children for her to babysit, you could let her sleep."

"Her dad gave her a sleeping bag last year. I think she'd love to take that with her and 'camp out' in the house somewhere."

"Now you're thinking! Get creative. You will find solutions. Then make sure to run all of this by Tammie. Get her thoughts as well. She's your upline and your mentor. I promise you that she's dealt with this before. I'm sure she'll have some great guidance."

"Do you remember *The Consistency Rule*?" asked Belle.

"I do. You can't control a lot of things. But you *can* control how consistent you are."

"That's right. When you come up with a plan that meets the needs of your business… meaning that you get your tastings done, while at the same time you make sure that everything aligns with your core value of spending time with Michaela, your solution will work for both of you. Then you do those things consistently."

Kai said, "I'll touch base with Tammie when we hang up. Then Michaela and I will make our plan. Thank you so much, Belle. You're amazing!"

Belle laughed and fluffed her hair.

"It's the hair, isn't it? It's my totally amazing hair!"

Kai chuckled and replied, "Yes. It's the hair. And the wonderful heart of the lady who brushes it."

Belle said, "Wait! You know my hairdresser is a man, right?"

Both laughed. Kai said, "You're so corny! You remind me of Michael! Okay, let's say the wonderful heart of the lady who wears it."

The ladies said their goodbyes and finished their call.

Kai closed her laptop and decided to get a glass of iced tea.

Walking up to the refrigerator, she noticed water oozing out from underneath.

Great! Now what do I do?

She pulled the appliance out from the wall, and a hose of some sort came loose and began to spray water all over her.

Kai screamed.

It wasn't a fearful scream.

It was the kind of scream, combined with a little bit of laughter, that happens when someone is unexpectedly sprayed with a water hose.

There was a knock on the door.

There was another knock.

The doorbell rang twice.

Kai wished that her front door came equipped with voicemail, because she certainly couldn't leave to go answer.

Finally, the door opened. It was the new neighbor.

"Is everything alright? I was passing by and I heard a scream. Can I help?"

"Yes! Please come into the kitchen!"

The man followed her voice into the kitchen.

Seeing her predicament, he asked, "May I?"

Kai backed away from the refrigerator, and the man reached down low and turned the water-control valve that fed the ice maker to the off position.

The water immediately stopped spraying.

Kai and the new neighbor looked at each other. They were completely soaked.

"Hi. I'm Dalton Henderson," he said, as he reached out to shake Kai's hand.

"Kai Frazier." She shook his hand.

With a very serious look, Dalton said, "Nice to meet you Kai Frazier. Now, I have a very important question to ask you."

Kai raised an eyebrow and asked, "What?"

Dalton's face transformed from serious to lighthearted. Kai noticed that he had a very nice smile.

"May I please borrow a towel?"

"Of course," said Kai, almost embarrassed that she hadn't already thought to get one.

Kai retrieved a couple of beach towels from the laundry room cabinet and returned.

Handing one of the towels to Dalton, she asked, "Is it serious?"

Dalton replied as he wiped his face, "No. I'll be fine. It's just water."

She crossed her arms, nodded her head, smirked and said, "I'm glad you won't need surgery. I was talking about the refrigerator. Do I need to call a plumber?"

Dalton smiled. "Not at all. It's an easy repair."

Dalton thought for a minute, remembering that when he had seen Kai and Michaela in the neighborhood, it was only the two of them. He had never seen a man around.

"You know, I could repair it for you. But I have a better idea."

"What?" said Kai, becoming just a little bit suspicious.

"Instead of me doing the repair for you, why don't I show you what I would do in the same situation?"

"What do you mean?"

Dalton answered, "Well, I'm a little embarrassed to admit it but I'm not very mechanically inclined."

"I thought you said you could fix this."

"Oh. I can. But I would rather teach you what I do when I don't know how to do something…" Laughing, he said, "Which is actually most things."

Kai's face and demeanor relaxed just a bit.

"Let's do an online search and find a video that shows us what we should do."

Kai said, "Okay. That makes sense."

The two walked over to the table and Kai opened her laptop again.

After watching a couple of home repair videos online, Kai said, "So we need to replace the ice maker hose. That looks simple enough."

Dalton said, "I have to go to the hardware store to get a couple of things. If it's alright with you, I'll pick up a hose for your refrigerator and bring it back by. Then if you'd like, we can do the repair together. Does that sound like a good plan?" he asked.

Deciding to accept the help, Kai replied, "Yes it does. Thank you."

While Dalton was away, Kai used more towels and a mop to clear the water from the floor.

After about an hour, Dalton returned. Handing the hose and a couple of tools to Kai, he asked, "Ready to do this?"

"I am," answered Kai, trying to sound more confident that she really felt.

Dalton moved the refrigerator so that they could access the back. Then the two neighbors began the repair.

"Would it be alright if I asked you something?" Dalton asked, with slight hesitation.

Kai answered without looking away from her work.

"Sure."

"I don't want to come across as being overly nosey or too forward."

"Go ahead."

"Okay. When I saw you and your daughter…"

"Michaela."

"Okay, thanks. When I saw you and Michaela playing in the snow, I didn't see anyone else. I'm not trying to pay too much attention or anything, but I don't think I've ever seen anyone else here."

Dalton was getting uncomfortable and wishing that he had waited to start this particular conversation some other time. His awkwardness was actually making Kai happy. She wasn't interested in having a man in her life right now, but she also liked knowing that she could still make one a little nervous.

"I have friends over."

"No. That's not what I mean. What I'm trying to ask, in the most inept way… is there a Mr. Frazier in the picture?"

Kai looked up at Dalton, tilted her head a little and gave him a quizzical look.

"You know, I could give you that answer. But instead, why don't I show you what I would do in this same situation… one where I didn't know how to do something. Let's do an online search for, 'How to ask a woman if she's married without fumbling for the right words.' We can watch a couple of videos. Then you can try again."

Embarrassed, Dalton looked down and smiled at Kai. He nodded his head in agreement and said, "I think that would probably be a good idea."

"I'm a widow. My husband passed away almost a year ago."

"Oh. I am so sorry. I didn't know."

Kai, having finished the hose repair stood up and said, "Thank you. For both the condolences and the repair guidance."

Sensing that she needed to throw Dalton a lifeline and rescue him from the awkwardness of the moment, Kai asked, "How about you? Is there a significant other in your life? I haven't seen anyone over there either."

Kai immediately regretted letting it slip that she too had been paying attention.

Damn!

Dalton, on the other hand, was surprised and glad that she had noticed. Though he was careful not to allow his thoughts to reveal themselves in his expression. Like a poker player who had just been dealt pocket aces, he didn't want to let it be seen that his heart may have just skipped a beat.

"No. No Mrs. Henderson. There was once. Not anymore."

"Divorced?"

Dalton sighed.

"No. Car accident about four years ago."

"I'm sorry."

"Me too."

"Girlfriend?"

"No. I haven't even really dated that much. Mostly, when I have gone out, I've just gone places with good friends. I guess I've just not been in a hurry. We had a great relationship. I'm hesitant to try again. I think maybe I'm afraid that a new relationship wouldn't be as good. Until I can get past that… it would be insensitive on my part to start anything new."

Hmm. Thoughtful. Unexpected.

Kai looked at Dalton and nodded her head.

"I get it. I understand completely."

There were no words for a few seconds.

Then Michaela came through the front door. "Hi, Mom! I'm back!"

Thankful for the interruption, Kai said, "In the kitchen, honey!"

Seeing the surprise on Michaela's face as she entered the room, Kai said, "Michaela, this is our new neighbor, Dalton Henderson. Dalton, this is my daughter, Michaela."

Dalton said, "Very nice to meet you, Michaela."

Michaela said nothing.

Kai frowned. "Manners?"

"Nice to meet you too, Mr. Henderson."

Silence.

"Dalton heard me yell when a hose on the back of the refrigerator broke, and he came over to check on me. Then he graciously helped me learn how to do the repair."

Silence.

Dalton broke the silence.

"Well, it looks like you have everything under control, Kai. So I will head on out. Nice meeting everyone."

"Thanks again, Dalton."

Once the door closed, Michaela looked at Kai and gave her a little smile.

"I told you he was checking you out."

Kai shook her head. "Don't you have some homework?"

Michaela laughed and headed to her room.

9

Standing close to a brick wall creates a very limited field of vision.

That can be uncomfortable to a certain extent. Maybe even claustrophobic.

Yet, for Kai, the benefit of that viewpoint was that it allowed her to easily see each individual brick, the pattern created by the mason and the intricate detail of even the smallest bits of clay. The downside, however, was that she could only see that which was directly in front of her.

But as she took a few steps back and her eyes adjusted, the definition of each brick began to blur and soften until the narrow portion which was once the entire focus of her attention became only a small fragment of a larger design.

The reason? Her perspective changed as the distance increased.

As she progressed through her life, she found that her perspective changed in much the same way.

This was certainly the way it seemed to Kai as she thought about the last fifteen months.

During the days and weeks immediately following Michael's death, all she could do was fix her attention on the moments directly in front of her. She struggled to take even one step… and then another… just trying to get through each day without allowing her heartbreak and uncertainty to bring her to a complete emotional stop.

There was so much pain.

There was also so much… numbness.

The irony of that emotional combination was not lost on Kai.

How could someone experience such pain… and yet feel so incredibly numb at the same time? It would seem that the two could not exist together.

And yet, that was exactly how Kai felt in those early days.

But now, although she still missed Michael very much, Kai found it easier to take those steps each day.

As the weeks and months progressed, just like stepping back from that brick wall, her perspective was changed by the healing effect of time. The dark and difficult view which had once consumed her entire focus had now become a less vivid part of a larger and brighter picture.

She had Michaela to heal with as well. She wasn't going through this experience alone. That was a sweet and wonderful comfort.

She also had her mom and dad, of course. And Lindsay was there. When she felt that she was on the verge of not being able to carry on, their love and support for her seemed to provide an almost heroic lift to her soul.

The hours trudged into days.

The days lumbered into weeks.

And the weeks drifted into months.

Here she was, a little over a year later, being able to smile, laugh, and feel the beginnings of what would someday feel like a normal life again.

She knew that healing was the right thing to do. It was definitely what Michael would have wanted. But there were times, especially on days when she felt a little more *normal*, that her relief was mixed with just a pinch of useless guilt.

Tonight, however, was not one of those times.

The past few months had gone very well for Kai. Her new career was really starting to take off. Michaela had become a great partner and was extremely helpful in so many ways. The two ladies had also found the right balance in how often Michaela could accompany Kai in the evenings. They were spending lots of time together and that made them both happy.

So, on this evening, Kai was enjoying a night out with her mom, her dad, Michaela, and Lindsay. The five of them were celebrating Michaela's eleventh birthday, and her move up to the sixth grade.

Since it was her bash, Michaela picked the place. Thus the group was having dinner at her favorite steakhouse — The Bull and Brew.

The server came to the table to take the group's order.

Taking all four ladies' orders first, the server then turned to Kai's father, Allen.

"What may I get for you tonight, sir?"

"I believe I will have the 'Bull and Brew's Best.'"

"That would be the ribeye, would it sir?"

"Yes ma'am. Let's make it the twelve ounce, please."

"And how would you like that cooked?"

"Cook it in a way that reminds me of those times I actually win an argument with my wife."

"That would be *rare*, would it sir?"

"That's right, young lady. That would be rare indeed."

Everyone at the table started laughing.

Kathy said, "I'm just glad he didn't order his steak like he usually does."

"How's that?" asked Lindsay.

Kathy replied, "He normally orders his rare steak by saying, "Honey, tell the chef to break his horns off, wipe his backside and send him to the table."

"That would be rare, alright!" said Lindsay, laughing.

Allen said, "Now wait just a minute! I need to correct the record on this! That is not true!"

"What?" asked Kathy, with a surprised look.

"I do not use the word 'backside'! That word does not leave my mouth!"

Everyone laughed, but Michaela shook her head.

"That's not true, Grandpa. Do you remember picking us up at the airport last year? You used the word 'backside' then when Grandma wouldn't let you say 'horse's ass' in front of me."

Everyone burst into laughter. Everyone except Kai, that is.

"Young lady?"

Knowing where this was going, Michaela replied innocently, "What? I *am* eleven now, you know."

"I don't care. There will be no more of that."

"Yes, ma'am.

"Mom?"

"Yes?"

"When I am fifteen, will I be allowed to say 'ass' if I want to order a rare steak? Or is that just the year when coffee will no longer make my feet stink?"

Everyone laughed again. Even Kai snickered a little but tried to hide it from Michaela.

As the server poured the adults a glass of Cabernet Sauvignon, Kai said, "Changing the subject, I have some news to share."

"What news?" asked her mother.

Looking at Michaela, she said, "Well, my partner and I have really gotten our wine business going quite well. Much better than I expected this early on."

Michaela exclaimed, "That's right, Grandma and Grandpa! We're kicking some serious…"

Kai raised an eyebrow.

"Uh… backside!" finished Michaela.

Returning the conversation to her mom and dad, Kai said, "That is true. We are. And I've been offered a promotion. They would like for me to start recruiting and training a team."

"That's great!" said Allen. "I'm very proud of you, Kai!"

Congratulations circled the table.

Kai lifted both of her hands to slow the conversation.

"I haven't actually decided to accept the offer yet."

Kathy said, "Whether you do, or whether you don't, the fact that they recognize that you're doing a great job and that you have a lot to offer others is wonderful, Kai. I'm proud of you too!"

"Why wouldn't you accept the offer?" asked Allen.

"I may," replied Kai. "But the most important thing in the world to me is my eleven-year-old business partner. She and I haven't had a chance to discuss it yet. This is a decision we will make together. We've found a really good mix of how we're doing things. It is working very well."

Turning to Michaela, Kai said, "If taking that promotion is going to hurt our partnership in any way, I'll turn it down."

Michaela leaned back in her seat, propped her elbows on the chair's arms, and interlaced her fingers.

Nodding and with a serious look, she said, "I think we should discuss that at our next board meeting. Would you agree?"

"I would," replied Kai.

"Then I will add the item to our agenda."

The other adults laughed. But Kai just smiled and looked at her daughter.

Oh… I love you so much.

Later that night, while Kai was sitting in her bed and reading, she heard a light knock on the side of her doorway.

"May I come in?"

"Of course, baby."

Kai lifted the bed covers, inviting Michaela to join her. Michaela crawled in.

"Mom, I think it'll be alright if you take that promotion."

"You do?"

"I do. But let me ask you something. If you take it, and we decide we don't like it, can you give it back?"

"Mm-hmm. I can."

Michaela sat up with her back against the headboard.

"Mom?"

"Yes?"

"I want to tell you something."

"Okay."

"Last year… after dad… after dad died."

Kai just nodded.

"I wasn't so sure that we'd be okay. I was scared, mom. And I cried a lot in my room."

"I know, baby."

Kai had often heard Michaela's tears from outside her bedroom door. Sometimes she would go inside and comfort her. And at other times, she instead gave her space.

Michaela was struggling to find the right words.

"Mom. I know we're gonna be okay now. We kind of already are."

Kai said nothing.

"I just wanted you to know that I'm really proud of you. I brag about you to my friends. I love watching you in front of people at the wine tastings. You're really good at all of that. I'm glad you're my mom."

Michaela curled up beside her mom.

"Me too, Michaela. I'm also very proud of you. And I love you to the moon and back."

"I love you, too."

With that, Michaela fell asleep in the safest place in the world… in her mother's arms.

The next day, Kai had her weekly call with Belle. But instead of the meeting being in the afternoon to allow for the time difference between Texas and Hawaii, the call was scheduled to be in the morning at 9:00. When Kai got the email, she noted the difference and, at first, wondered if it was a mistake.

The time was no mistake. Belle was traveling and was in Manhattan.

Looking past Belle's image on the screen and seeing a hotel room, Kai said, "I am so not used to seeing you anywhere except on a beach, Belle. Where are you?"

"I'm at the Marriott Marquis in New York! It's literally right on Times Square!"

"Oh, wow! Michael and I stayed there once years ago. It was nice being so close to all of the restaurants and Broadway shows. So, why are you there?"

"I'm part of a quartet of women… not the singing kind but the speaking kind… who'll share a stage tonight at the Direct Selling World Alliance Coach Excellence School."

"That's awesome!"

"Thank you! We've all built successful businesses, but from different direct sales companies. But we have one really great thing in common."

"What's that?"

"We are women who take the time to mentor other women in business and life."

"Well, that's certainly what you've done for me. I am truly grateful and not at all surprised that you'd be on that stage."

Belle said, "There are so many of us out there who are always willing to help. Don't get me wrong. There are some great successful men out there who are also ready, willing, and able to mentor. Many of them are my friends. But those of us onstage tonight just have such a heart for helping other women start a career or business and then making it a success. We want to invite others to join us. So tonight's agenda is a panel discussion called, 'Ladies Night at the DSWA.' And they gave the topic a subtitle that I just love: 'Slay Your Own Dragons — Handsome Prince Optional.'"

"Wow! I would love to see that!"

"You actually can! The event will be livestreamed. I'll send you the link to watch."

"That would be great!"

Kai continued, "I have some news to share. I've been offered a promotion. Special Memories Wine Club would like for me to start recruiting and build my own sales team."

"Congratulations! It is an honor to be asked! Have you decided to take the position?"

"Not yet. But I am considering it. Michaela and I had a 'board meeting' last night. She's encouraging me to take the promotion as long as I can 'give it back' if she or I decide it's not working for us."

"Bright kid! I knew I liked that girl! So how are you feeling about the idea?" asked Belle.

Kai thought for a moment and said, "On one hand, I like the idea. The extra money would be great. I like the feeling I get from being asked to take on the responsibility. And, as long as it works for Michaela and me, I love the idea of my daughter seeing me become a leader of a team that we build."

Kai smiled. "She actually told me that she was proud of me last night!"

"I don't blame her! I'm proud of you too!"

"Thank you."

Belle asked, "Well, that's on one hand. What's on the other?"

Kai replied, "Just a little bit of doubt in my ability to do the job. I've never recruited before. I've never led a team of people either."

Belle let a couple of seconds pass and then asked, "Think back to when you first started. Did you have any doubts about your ability to do the job you are doing now?"

"Yes. I certainly did."

"Do you have the confidence that you're doing the job well now?"

"Yes."

Belle said, "If you had allowed your doubts to keep you from taking a chance, where would you be today?"

Kai didn't answer. She just raised her eyebrows and nodded.

"Kai, you are a very sharp woman with a keen sense of what people are feeling. Your empathy level is high. And, because people can feel your sincere interest in them, they really like you.

"You're also a hardworking person. As I often say, you can't hide hard work in direct sales. It shows up for everyone to see. That's why you've been offered this promotion. That will also set a fantastic example for those who join your team. Don't allow a little thing like doubting yourself keep you from making a decision that you truly believe would be in the best interest of you and Michaela."

"That makes sense," said Kai.

Belle said, "You mentioned that Tammie had taught you how to connect people with each other at your tastings. Are you good at making that happen?"

"I am. It's actually my favorite part of the evening."

"Do people follow your lead as you're doing that? Or do they ignore you and do their own thing?"

Kai smiled. "They tend to follow me."

"Well that tells me two things. You're only a leader if people will follow... and they already do. So leadership shouldn't be an issue. Sure, you'll have to learn things. But you can do that. You've also laid the foundation for one of your best ways to recruit."

"What do you mean?"

"As you are making those connections, you're going to find people who will say things that let you know they are looking for a career change or a 'side-hustle.' As they tell you where they work, they may say something about not being completely happy. Or they may mention the need for more income for some reason. Ask questions that get them to open up about those things and then listen. Then make the connection for them. You'll still be connecting people. But in this case, the connection you make will be between them and your company to earn an income... through you."

"That makes sense to me," said Kai.

Belle said, "One more thing on that topic. When you're doing your tastings, your focus doesn't really start with the wine, does it?"

"No. I begin with getting them to tell some of their favorite stories involving wine. I focus more on the things they like to do. Then I bring our wine into the story as a way to help them make those times even more enjoyable."

"Exactly! Recruiting is no different. You focus on how they want their lives to be. Becoming a part of your team is just a way you can help them get there. You've been selling the vision of people enjoying their life experiences more—with wine. And now, you'll also be

selling an opportunity in which people can build the life they want…
by helping others enjoy their life experiences more—with wine."

Kai nodded her head.

"Since you're considering taking a promotion, this is an opportune
time to teach you our next rule."

"Great! I'm listening."

"Rule number six is *The Rising Tide Rule.* A rising tide lifts all
boats. Be that tide."

"Explain, please," said Kai.

"Be willing to share your knowledge and experience with others.
It is easy to share with members of your team. Their success will
directly impact your income. But also be willing to share with those
whose success will have no bearing on your business. Give from your
heart and your wisdom with the sincere desire that something you say
truly makes someone else's life better."

Kai said, "I like that rule. That's pretty much what you've been
doing for me over the last year."

Belle smiled and said, "That's right. By the way, there is one
exception to that rule."

"What's that?"

"When it comes to your friends and family, refrain from giving
advice about how they should live their lives unless you have their
permission to do so. Otherwise, you may need to wear protective
gear!"

Laughing, Kai said, "I'll remember that, Belle!"

Belle began to close out their call.

"I have to run. There are a couple of meetings I committed to attending. Then I'm going to see a matinee of a play with Hugh Jackman and Daniel Craig!"

"Have fun! I wish I were there with you!"

"Maybe you can join us next year," said Belle. "I'll send you the link for tonight's livestream."

As Kai said goodbye and turned off her computer, she realized that she had much to think about.

The day passed quickly into evening.

As they prepared dinner, Kai asked Michaela, "There's a business event tonight that I'd like for us to watch. Are you up for it?"

"Sure," replied Michaela.

Kai said nothing else about the event. She wanted Belle's appearance to be a surprise.

After dinner, the two ladies settled onto the sofa with a large bowl of popcorn and two bottles of water. Kai booted her laptop, and then shared the screen with their main television. They were just in time. The livestream of the DSWA meeting was about to begin.

There was loud and upbeat music playing, and the crowd seemed to be really enjoying the atmosphere. Spotlights of white, red, blue, and green were sweeping across the room. It reminded Kai of those Hollywood award shows, full of glitz and excitement.

As the music died down, the crowd turned its attention to the stage and the announcer began.

"Ladies and gentlemen, welcome to Ladies Night at the DSWA!"

The crowd cheered like happy fans at a large sporting event.

"We have a very special panel discussion tonight with four FABULOUS and extremely successful women. The topic for the night? Slay Your Own Dragons — Handsome Prince Optional!"

The crowd again lifted cheers, with added laughter.

Michaela said, "That looks like a lot of fun!"

"It does, doesn't it?"

The announcer brought each woman out onto the stage with a short introduction about who they were and their business success. When he brought Belle out onto the stage, Michaela yelled.

"Mom! Look! That's Belle!"

Kai replied as she laughed, "I know! That's why I wanted us to watch it together."

Each of the four ladies were given a few minutes to tell a little of their personal story. Some made Kai and Michaela laugh. Some made them think. And, true to form, Belle made them do both.

"Years ago," Belle began, "I was speaking to a crowd about this size. I had on a pair of brand-new shoes that were so beautiful and stylish. They were gorgeous. However, what they were not... was comfortable. Don't you hate beautifully uncomfortable shoes?"

The crowd gave back a resounding "YES!"

"So I am going to do the same thing today as I did back then."

Still holding the microphone, Belle reached down with one hand, pulled the pins from the buckles, loosened the straps and removed both of her shoes... one at a time.

She held the shoes up, showing them to the crowd, and she tossed them offstage to the left.

Kai and Michaela laughed as the crowd began to cheer.

Belle walked out to the front edge of the stage, looked down at her feet and wiggled her toes.

"I do this wiggling my toes thing when I am at my office… which is the beach at Poipu in Kauai, Hawaii. It relaxes me and helps me get the day going better."

Michaela exclaimed, "Mom! You do that!"

Kai just smiled.

Belle talked a few minutes about the value of women mentoring other women and then returned to her tall chair which closely resembled a director's chair on a movie set.

Once each lady had spoken, the emcee took questions from the audience.

Most of the questions were on business and mentoring topics. Each of the panelists gave answers from their particular perspective.

A lady in the audience asked the first question.

"Hi. My name is Aniyah. My question is how would you suggest I help the women on my team get their husbands to be more supportive of their businesses?"

Belle answered first.

"Hi Aniyah. Let's roleplay that one just a little. The first thing I would ask them to answer would be, 'Could you define *being supportive* for me?'"

Belle gestured to Aniyah to answer.

Aniyah said, "Doing things like… maybe helping out at trade shows or helping distribute brochures with them."

Belle smiled a little and said, "Then I would say, 'May I ask you another question?'"

"Sure."

"Do you go to your husband's job and help him do his work?"

Aniyah smiled and said, "Most would say, no. Of course not!"

Belle said, "Sometimes we can allow ourselves to define being supportive as helping us do our regular work tasks. That definition is too narrow. The truth is that there are many ways for a spouse to be supportive without that specific requirement."

Gwynne, one of the other panelists, chimed in as well.

"It also may depend on other factors. Like, whether or not they are both working jobs, and how they divvy up the household chores and take care of any children. But my favorite coaching to give in that scenario is for the women to start taking on the responsibility of some specific household bills — and paying for them directly from the profits of their business. It doesn't matter if it is the electric bill or the mortgage. Just have them start at a level that makes sense for them. Once they do that, they will often find that their husband becomes *very* supportive."

A voice from the crowd shouted, "Yours certainly did!"

Gwynne replied, "Aww... I love you too, baby! That's my husband out there."

Everyone laughed.

The questions continued for another ten minutes or so.

"We have time for one more question," said the emcee.

A young man raised his hand, received a microphone and asked, "I realize that the topic for tonight is 'Slay Your Own Dragons — Handsome Prince Optional,' but I'd like to ask... who up there is married and who is single?"

Looking around at the other panelists and taking a quick poll, Belle said, "It seems to be a fifty-fifty split up here. Two are married and two are single."

Belle smiled and said, "Are you just curious? Or are you prospecting?"

The crowd in the room broke out into laughter. The crowd on the sofa did as well.

The young man blushed and smiled.

"Maybe a little bit of both."

More laughter.

Belle looked over at Marion, the other single lady on the panel. "Marion, you're newly single. Would you like to take this one?"

Marion said, "Are you asking if I'd like to take the question? Or the man?"

Belle laughed.

"Your pick."

Marion looked at the young man, shook her head and smiled.

"I'm sorry, honey. You're cute. But I'm taking the question."

The room erupted in laughter once more.

Marion said, "I'll tell you a quick, funny story. I am recently divorced. I used the same attorney's firm for my divorce that I have used for several other matters over the years. Since I didn't know any divorce lawyers, my usual attorney referred me to someone else in his firm. Last week, I dropped by on a real-estate matter with my normal guy. As I was waiting in the foyer, the attorney who handled my divorce walked by.

"He said, 'Well, hello Marion! How are you?'

"I smiled and said, 'Doing well, thanks.'

"The receptionist saw this and said, 'I didn't know that you two knew each other.'

"He replied, 'We do. I'm the man that put that smile back on her face!'"

After the laughter died back down, Belle began to speak.

"Sometimes, when I talk about being single, I will have people misunderstand my intent. For me personally, I prefer being single. That is not to say that I am against marriage at all... especially when it is a good one."

Smiling and fluffing her hair, Belle said, "I stay single because I am just AWESOME at the job."

The audience laughed.

"Seriously, I am my best me as a single person. When it comes to this specific topic of women mentoring other women, I'm very passionate about mentoring all women, regardless of their relationship status, in building successful careers and businesses. I coach them to build their careers to whatever level makes their lives more stable and richer — not just financially but emotionally as well. The best marriages are normally those in which the two individuals grow and strive to become the best version of themselves, while at the same time supporting their partner's efforts in doing the same.

"It's funny. Even though single is the right choice for me, one of my favorite books that I have read in the last year is called, *The Go-Giver Marriage: A Little Story About the Five Secrets to Lasting Love*, by John David Mann and Ana Gabriel Mann. In their book, one of their points is that when two people build their individual lives — while also being the greatest supporter and cheerleader for each other — they find that part of their lives will overlap. That overlap can become the most beautiful and wonderful marriage for the two of them.

"My goal in mentoring women, whether they're married or not, is to equip them to become successful. That way, if a married woman should find that she is suddenly and unexpectedly single, she is in a good financial position. And if a single woman decides she wants to be in a relationship — it will be because she loves someone else… not because she needs anyone financially."

Belle continued, "I am currently mentoring a fabulous woman. She had an amazing and supportive spouse who was also a great father."

Kai and Michaela exchanged glances.

"Unfortunately, that good man passed away. So over the last year, she's been creating a new life for herself and her wonderful daughter. She's building an absolutely fantastic business in the wine industry. I am so proud of her! As a matter of fact, her upline is out there somewhere tonight."

Trying to shield her eyes from the lights, Belle looked across the room.

"Tammie, you know who I'm talking about. As you know, she is awesome. By the way, she thinks the world of you. So do I.

"I guess what I'm trying to say is that I want all women, even those in great marriages, to build wonderful lives that make them happy and prepare them for the future. And if I can help direct their path a little… that makes me happy. It's my way of making a tangible difference in the world. It's congruent with my values… the way I want to live my life. And I encourage and invite each of you who have achieved success in your business to do exactly the same."

Kai looked at Michaela and said, "That pretty much settles it for me. I think I'll take that promotion."

Michaela smiled and said, "I think you should."

10

Kai loved the change of seasons.

It didn't really matter which season was retiring, nor which was entering anew. She simply loved the transformation.

Late fall into early winter always ran at a frenzied pace because of the holidays. Family gatherings, preparing her favorite dishes, and shopping for just the right Christmas gift for each member of the family took on the feel of a series of sporting events for her. She loved the excitement.

February and March saw the cool temperatures and uncommon snows of winter yielding to the warm days and dramatic colors of spring. With that change, she felt a sense of renewal that gave fuel to her spirit.

In May, the hectic school schedules gave way to the slower, warm and fun days of summer. That shift rekindled Kai's memories of many wonderful vacations as a child and an adult.

But Kai's favorite transition by far was when the sweltering days of August, which could be brutal in Texas, finally bowed to the onset of fall. Although the days could still get warm, she began to feel a coolness in the air — especially in the early mornings and late evenings.

September had hurriedly departed just as October arrived, and flyers detailing the various fall festivals in the area were in Kai's mailbox on almost a daily basis.

Business was going great!

Over the last couple of months, Kai's new team had gotten off to a great start. In only eight weeks, she had four new recruits. Each of them were people she had met at the wine tastings she had been holding in the evenings. Two of the new recruits were ladies who had hosted tastings in their homes.

One of her new recruits was a guest at a tasting. Kai, as usual, was visiting with the attendees prior to the meeting and attempting to make connections happen where she could. One of those in attendance, Amy, happened to mention that she wanted to earn extra money for a family vacation. Kai showed her how she could help and she was excited to come aboard.

Thank you, Belle, for that great tidbit of coaching.

Kai's fourth recruit was a young man who had recently moved into the area and had been searching unsuccessfully for a new job. He had attended an additional tasting hosted by Lindsay. After the meeting, Derek asked Kai, "I like wine and I enjoy people. Can I make a full-time living doing this?"

"Absolutely!" she replied.

"You have to be willing to work hard and listen to your coaching. But if that describes you, I would be glad to have you on my team. I will help you with every step along the way. Someone had to teach me… and I will pass that along to you."

Kai laughed as she thought, *How am I going to teach Derek the miniskirt rule?*

Kai and Michaela had made the decision together that they would limit the weeknight events to two or three, and only have one event on the weekend. They felt that this balance was right for both of them.

To accomplish her goal of getting her new recruits trained, Kai would make sure that at least one of her team members was with her at each wine tasting she held. When appropriate, she would have more. She would also attend their first tastings, just as Tammie had done for her. Although her newbies still had much to learn, they were doing quite well... especially when Kai considered their limited tenure on the team.

When Belle coached Kai about training, she said, "One of the best ways you can train your new people is for you to never be alone. Invite someone to attend every tasting you're doing. That way, they see you model the behavior for them. As your team grows, you'll have some people that will be more active than others. Give those who are putting in the most effort the majority of your time. But you can always invite someone who still hasn't quite caught on yet, or someone who has become somewhat inactive, to one of your tastings. You'll often find that this simple act can rejuvenate their excitement and get them going again."

On this particular Wednesday evening in October, Kai and Michaela were having a nice quiet evening at home. The ladies were sitting on the front porch and enjoying the wonderful weather.

Kai was having a glass of Pinot Noir as she observed a few of her neighbors walking in the cul-de-sac. Michaela was enjoying a glass of lemonade and reading a book of short stories for her English class.

As Michaela looked up from her book, she noticed Dalton walking their way.

Dalton had become a friend to their family. When Kai needed help with any type of household repair, and was not able to find a video online that would show her what to do, she had become comfortable asking Dalton for his advice. She still didn't want Dalton to do the actual work, and he easily accepted that boundary. Kai believed that he actually respected her even more because of it. Nonetheless, she appreciated his guidance and was thankful for his friendship.

On more than one occasion, Dalton had said, "Hey, I don't know how to do a lot of things. I'm not the most mechanically minded person in the world. But I'm always willing to help you two if I can."

As he walked up the sidewalk, Michaela said, "Hi, Dalton!"

"Hello ladies! What's happening in your world tonight?"

Kai laughed and said, "Look around you, silly boy! It's the same thing that's happening in your world tonight too."

Dalton looked around the neighborhood and said, "That is so weird! The world looks completely different from your side of the street."

Giving Kai a phony puzzled look, he asked, "Are you sure that's right?"

"Yes I am," replied Kai, as she laughed. "What's that in your hand? Did the mailman put my mail in your box again?"

Holding up a sealed envelope and a bright orange flyer, Dalton replied, "Yes. And no. Yes… here's your mail. And no, this is your invitation to a party I'm throwing for the neighborhood."

Dalton handed the envelope and flyer to Kai.

Kai looked at the flyer and began to read aloud. "Dalton Henderson's First Annual Fall Festival/Halloween Party. Come as you are or dress up in your favorite costume. I will provide the meat and the drinks. You bring your favorite side dish or dessert. If you don't celebrate Halloween, consider this a Fall Festival. If you do celebrate Halloween, don your best costume. Either way, let's all get together and enjoy the evening."

Dalton said, "I plan on smoking a brisket and some sausages. I'll also grill some hotdogs and hamburgers. I've given the flyers to almost everyone in the neighborhood. It looks to be a good-sized group. I'd love to have the two of you join me if you are available."

"Let me check with my business partner." Kai looked over at Michaela and asked, "Would you check the calendar and see if we're available a week from Saturday?"

Kai already knew the answer. They were available.

"Let me see," replied Michaela, as she opened the calendar on her phone. "Oh, I'm sorry, Dalton. It looks like we have a wine tasting that night."

Dalton tried to hide his disappointment. Kai tried to hide her surprise. But Michaela looked like a novice poker player who had just unsuccessfully bluffed.

Smiling, she said, "I'm kidding. We're available. Can we go, Mom?"

Kai smiled and said, "We'd love to come. Thanks for inviting us, Dalton."

"Great!" he said.

Kai asked, "Why don't I help with the drinks? I'll bring wine. I have connections in that industry."

145

Dalton laughed and said, "Yes you do, don't you?"

Michaela said in her very businesslike tone, "That's me. I'm her connection."

They all laughed, said their goodbyes, and Dalton continued his delivery of the flyers.

Michaela looked at Kai and asked, "Do you like Dalton?"

"Of course I do. He's a good friend to have around."

"Mom, that's not what I meant. I mean do you *like* Dalton?"

Kai smiled at her daughter and said, "I don't think I am ready to *like* anybody in that way yet, Michaela. But if that time ever comes, you'll be the first person I discuss it with."

"Well, that makes sense to me. After all, I *am* your business partner," Michaela said with a faint grin.

"Oh, no. You're much more than that, baby. You're my forever partner."

Michaela returned to reading her book and Kai returned to watching the happenings in the neighborhood.

On Friday afternoon, Kai had another call with Belle.

"Good morning!" said Kai.

"Good afternoon!" replied Belle.

"So what's happening in Poipu today?"

Belle replied, "Oh, it's a beautiful morning. I've been watching three novice surfers that are very entertaining. They struggle to get up on the board. They stay on for about five seconds. Then they crash and burn!"

"That sounds like fun!"

"For me, maybe. Not so much for the surfers!"

Kai said, "Oh, I don't know. Falling off a surfboard in Hawaii would be more fun than standing on solid ground just about anywhere else. Speaking of Poipu," she continued, "We're planning on coming back out in December for our annual family trip."

"That's great! I can't wait to see you all!"

Kai said, "Lindsay will be coming as well."

"Awesome! I'll have you all over for dinner!"

"That sounds like a wonderful plan!" Kai replied.

Belle asked, "So what would you like to talk about today?"

Kai thought for a moment and replied, "I don't really have a lot on my list. Things are going pretty well. I have four recruits. They're all putting in the effort it takes to build their business. They're hard workers with strong people skills. Overall, I'm pleased."

"What books do you have them reading?"

"I'm taking them through the same series of books that Tammie started me on. Then I added a couple more that you've mentioned."

"That's good. Are they reading them?"

"Yes." She smiled. "Although some a little slower than others."

"Remember to recommend great podcasts as well. Hearing authors and thought leaders on the subjects of sales and leadership can be a tremendous help to everyone."

"I will."

Kai thought for a second, and then said, "Belle. I do have something I'd like to get your thoughts on. Our business is built on a duplicatable model. As you know, it's similar to a franchise mentality. Do it the way that's been successful. Keep doing it that way. It's been successful before and helps to make your future success more predictable."

"Right," said Belle. "That is pretty consistent messaging across all direct sales companies. It reduces the chances for failure."

Kai said, "I understand that and I support the idea. That being said, I've been thinking about a couple of things lately that I believe would be pretty effective. But I also don't want to give anyone the impression that I'm not supportive of the processes we use."

"How much of a departure would your ideas be from the normal system? What would it change?"

"Actually, it wouldn't really change anything. It would be more like an addition to what we're already doing."

Belle said, "Explain."

"I'd like to start a networking group… maybe a better term would be a connecting group. Everyone who has ever attended one of my tastings would be invited. I could create an email list to communicate easily. We could have monthly gatherings to help people share about what they do in their business and see if we can connect people with each other. I can also see opening this group up to the people on my team. I think it would be a great thing to do for everyone. I believe it would help increase new sales and recruiting."

Belle asked, "I have no doubt you're right. So what are you worried about?"

"Just the fact that it is a departure from the norm. It isn't really what is being taught. I have also heard a couple of comments at meetings about making sure that we're following the system. I want to make sure that I support what we're already doing."

Belle considered what Kai had said.

"Kai. There's a difference in being creative as opposed to not supporting the system that is being taught in your organization."

"What do you mean?"

Belle replied, "I always tell my new recruits to spare me their creativity for the first ninety days. Do everything exactly as I teach them. Then after that ninety days, if they want to try something new, they'll hopefully have had enough successful experiences that they won't stray too far from what's bringing income to them. If they aren't willing to follow that coaching in the beginning, I tell them to try it my way first and prove me wrong. Then try it their way next and prove themselves right."

"Has anyone ever done that? Proven their way is better?"

Belle smiled. "Not yet."

She continued, "But don't confuse following a proven system that works as meaning that it's also a system that has no room for creativity. You have enough experience now that you can try some ideas out to see if they work. Decide what you want to do. Make a plan as to how it can become successfully implemented. Then talk with Tammie about your plan. Get her advice. Let her know about your desire to be faithful to your training, but at the same time get a little creative now and then."

Kai said, "That makes a lot of sense."

Belle asked, "Are you concerned that you will get into trouble for some reason?"

"Maybe. A little anyway."

"Perfect!" replied Belle. "That makes this the ideal time to teach you rule number seven!"

Kai asked, "Okay! What's rule number seven?"

Belle replied, "I'm glad you asked! Rule number seven is *The Naughty Rule.*"

Kai laughed. "This should be good!"

"It is! *The Naughty Rule* says, if you aren't getting in trouble once in a while, you simply aren't trying hard enough."

"Go on," said Kai as she laughed.

"Remember that innovation happens when gifted people follow their vision. Don't let, 'Because that's the way we've always done it' become your mantra. What would you do if you knew that you couldn't fail? Great things often happen because someone was creative and brave enough to try.

"I remember once getting into a little hot water with my local government when I decided to put up a sign in my yard advertising my business. It wasn't long before I got a letter informing me that my sign was on the right-of-way for the street in front of my house. As such, the sign must be removed."

"What did you do?" asked Kai.

Belle laughed. "I went to the local newspaper and television stations. I told them how the *big, mean government* had declared war on this independent business, which was owned by a local woman."

"You didn't!"

"Yes, I did! And I was getting so much attention in the press, it was a huge boost for my sales. Everyone wanted to do business with the lady who was standing up to the local government!"

"That is priceless!" said Kai.

"I eventually had to take the sign down, but the free advertising I got from the whole situation was incredible.

"Pay attention to wise counsel from your mentors. Then experiment. Try new methods. Stretch your mind and do things that get you out of your comfort zone. If that occasionally gets you into a little hot water — throw in some bubble bath, grab a glass of champagne, close your eyes and relax.

"By the way, there is something that I do that you may find very helpful. I send out cards to all of my clients, my team, and many of my business associates. I use a service where I can upload pictures that I think they would enjoy… often that I find on social media. I can put a custom message on each card. Then the service prints and mails the cards for me. It's a low monthly fee and all of my contacts really seem to love it when they receive them."

Kai said, "That sounds like a great idea! I will call Tammie as soon as we get through and run my thoughts by her."

"That sounds great," said Belle. "I'd better run now. These surfer guys are about to hurt themselves or some innocent bystanders. There's an officer on the beach waving them in. He doesn't look very happy with them."

Kai said, "That's okay. They are just trying something new. If they don't get into a little trouble now and then, they simply aren't trying hard enough! They're using *The Naughty Rule*!"

The two ladies laughed and finished their call. Kai closed her laptop and called Tammie. After hearing Kai's ideas, Tammie encouraged her to go ahead.

"You aren't actually being unfaithful to the system we use, Kai. You're just trying something innovative that could easily make things even better. Track what you're doing and be ready to share your results. This could very well be an idea that helps everyone do better in their businesses."

Kai remembered, *The Rising Tide Rule. A rising tide lifts all boats. Be that tide.*

Kai began the process of building her connections network that very day. As she contacted her new recruits with the idea, they were eager to help make things happen as well. She sent out emails to people who had attended any of her tastings and reserved the location for her first get together. She also signed up for the service that Belle had mentioned, which she could use to send out cards.

This is going to be a great idea!

11

A week passed by, and the night had arrived for Dalton's first annual fall festival/Halloween party.

Kai had originally decided not to wear a costume. However, after being coaxed by Michaela, she changed her mind, and the ladies dressed as two characters from the television series, *The Addams Family*... Morticia and Wednesday Addams. Both had on black wigs, dark mascara and white face makeup that resulted in a very pale and mysterious look. Kai was wearing a long black gown that had fabric at the bottom resembling that of a black-widow spider. And Michaela was wearing a black dress with oversized white lapels around the collar.

"This gown may be a little too form fitting," said Kai as she looked into the mirror.

"Mom, you look hot!"

Kai smiled.

"Dalton won't be able to get a single sentence out correctly tonight!" laughed Michaela.

"Oh, stop it," replied Kai.

True! she thought.

Kai decided that the they should arrive a little early to bring the wine and help Dalton set up for the event.

"Hi ladies! You two look amazing! But I wish you had worn costumes!"

"Ha ha!" said Michaela, mockingly.

"Seriously, those are great costumes. You guys look very… uh… scary… or chic… or something."

Michaela looked at her mom. "Men just never know the right words to say."

Turning back to Dalton, she said, "Beautiful. That's the word, Dalton. Beautiful."

Dalton nodded in agreement.

Trying not to look directly at Kai, he said, "Beautiful is exactly the right word."

Kai asked, "Where would you like for us to set up the wine?"

"Oh, I'm sorry," said Dalton as he reached for the box. "Let me get that."

Kai gave him a smile, along with a look that implied that he didn't need to say such a thing. She said, "Really? You do know that I do this for a living, right? I have carried cases of wine before."

Michaela chimed in. "That's right, Dalton. Even I can carry a case of wine."

Dalton smiled and said, "I believe you."

Then he smiled, looked at Kai and said, "My wanting to take the box has nothing to do with thinking that you ladies couldn't do the job. It has everything to do with the fact that, being a gentleman, I wanted to lend a hand."

Kai tilted her head slightly and gave Dalton a smile.

"Then, yes sir. You can take these. I will go back across the street and get a second case."

Dalton placed the box on a table already set up with paper plates, napkins, and plastic utensils. Then he returned to attending the smoker and the grill as Michaela began to unpack the wine bottles. She set them up in a display on a table as she had done many times with her mother.

Dalton walked over to Michaela and asked, "Do you need anything?"

"No. I've got everything here. Thanks, though."

Dalton paused for a moment.

"Michaela, I'd like to ask you a question."

"What?"

He continued, "I'd like to get your opinion about something."

"Okay," she said, stopping what she was doing and giving Dalton her attention.

Kai returned with the wine, stopping just out of sight near the gazebo behind Dalton's house… the gazebo built by Michael for the Markhams before Dalton had bought the home. Neither Michaela nor Dalton noticed that she was there. Neither did they know she could hear their conversation.

"I've known you and your mom for a while now. I think you both are pretty great. And… I was thinking about asking your mom out. I wanted to know your opinion…"

"You mean like asking her out on a date?"

"Yes. Like asking her out on a date."

Laughing, Michaela said, "Don't you think you should be asking mom for *her* opinion, rather than me?"

"Well, yes. But that's not exactly what I wanted your opinion on. From everything I've heard, your dad was a really great guy. I know you loved him very much."

Kai paid close attention as Dalton spoke.

"Your feelings really matter to me, Michaela. I know that it could be something you aren't ready for yet. I wanted to know how you might feel about the idea of me asking your mom to dinner and a movie."

Michaela thought for a minute and said, "I like you Dalton. You aren't like a lot of men I know. You admit when you don't know something. And you don't mind being a complete goofball when you feel awkward and uncomfortable."

"Like now?"

Michaela laughed. "Yes. Like now."

Michaela got a very serious look on her face and said, "Before I tell you my opinion, I need to ask you a very important question."

"Okay."

"Do you promise to have her home by curfew? If she comes in late, I'll have to ground her." Her serious look turned into a big smile.

Kai decided that she did not want the discussion to go any further… yet. So she made her presence known and walked toward the table.

"I'm back. What have you guys been talking about?"

Michaela and Dalton looked at each other and laughed.

"Movies," replied Michaela.

"Restaurants," replied Dalton.

Kai said, "Interesting. Well people will start arriving soon. Michaela, let's get the rest of the wine set up while Dalton finishes the food.

12

Kai was awakened by the flight attendant as the plane was entering its final descent into Honolulu's Daniel K. Inouye International Airport.

"It's time to bring your seatbacks and tray tables up," she said in a friendly and soft tone.

Kai looked to her left and saw her daughter playing video games on the console attached to the seat in front of her. Michaela didn't say anything. She just looked at her mother and smiled. To Kai's right, Lindsay was waking up as well.

"That was a nice nap," said Lindsay, as she stretched and yawned.

Kai nodded.

There would be a two-hour layover at the airport. Then the three ladies would board a connecting flight for their quick trip to Lihue, Kauai.

Kai wished she had planned a little extra time in Honolulu. She wanted to take Michaela and Lindsay to Pearl Harbor so that they could see the Arizona Memorial and tour the museum. She and Michael had gone twice.

Kai remembered Michael telling a friend once, "There are three places that I have visited where just the simple fact that I was standing there on the ground filled my eyes with tears. One was when I visited the Oklahoma City National Memorial, where the Alfred P. Murrah Federal Building was bombed. The second was at ground zero in New York City. And the third was standing atop the Arizona Memorial in Pearl Harbor, the final resting place for over a thousand crewmen who died when Japan attacked the U.S. and America's involvement in World War II began."

A day which will live in infamy, Kai thought, remembering the videos she had seen of President Franklin Delano Roosevelt's famous speech declaring war on Japan.

Kai wanted Michaela to visit those places as well. Partly because she wanted her daughter to grasp the magnitude and historical significance of the events. But mostly because those locations meant so much to her father.

Maybe I can rearrange our flight home so that we could have time to go.

There was plenty of time for the ladies to deplane, visit a couple of shops in the airport, and then board their flight to Lihue.

"We'll be there in less than an hour!" Michaela said excitedly, as she reviewed their itinerary. "Mom, can we hang out on the beach for a while this evening?"

"Of course, baby. And we will be here for an entire week, just like last year. We'll get lots of beach time."

Once landing in Lihue and retrieving their luggage, Kai sent a text to Belle.

"Landed in Lihue. Going to get checked in at the resort and hang out on the beach. May grab some dinner later. May just go to bed. Will you be on the beach tomorrow?"

After a couple of minutes, Belle's reply arrived.

"Yes. I'll be there. Want to drop by around 11:00? Also, does Wednesday work for having you all over for dinner?"

Kai replied, "Yes on dinner. See you tomorrow at 11:00."

Belle texted again, "Thanks so much for picking up my car at the airport. That is really helping me out. The keys will be at the ticket counter for American. The envelope has both of our names on it. See you in Poipu."

Just a few days prior, Belle had asked Kai if she would mind picking up a new car for her that was being delivered to the airport on the day of their arrival. "I still have my old one, so you guys can use it while you're here."

"I'll be glad to." said Kai. "And thanks so much for letting us use it for the week."

Lindsay and Michaela saw that Kai had been texting. Lindsay asked, "Were you texting Belle?"

"Yes. She's invited us to dinner on Wednesday, and I'll be meeting with her tomorrow at 11:00 on the beach."

"Can we go with you?" asked Michaela. "I would love to go ahead and meet her." added Lindsay.

Kai replied, "Sure you can. She'll be spending an hour with me and often has a tight schedule. But the two of you can come with me and I'll make the introductions. Then y'all can go have some fun while Belle and I visit."

"Cool!" exclaimed Michaela. "Lindsay, you 'll love Belle."

Lindsay replied, "I haven't even met her yet and I already do. She's been a great friend to my best friend!"

The keys were at the counter, just as Belle had said. The ladies located the car, loaded their luggage into the trunk and drove away from the airport.

"I love the smell of a new car," said Lindsay as she inhaled a deep breath. "This is nice too! Belle must be doing quite well!"

"She is, indeed. And part of the reason that I've had such a good year is because of her mentorship. She's an amazing person."

On the way to their resort, they made a quick stop at a local grocery store to pick up just a few essential supplies… coffee, wine, water, snacks, juice, and fresh fruit for breakfast. They would make another trip to the store on Monday to buy food for the week.

Once they arrived and checked in, Kai and Michaela took a walk on the beach while Lindsay drove to a local pizza shop to pick up their dinner.

As the setting sun dwindled down to the tiniest of lines on the horizon, the ladies opened the wine, the pizza, and the water, and enjoyed their dinner on the lanai.

"I can't believe I'm so tired," said Michaela.

"It's the time difference," replied Lindsay. "It may only be 8:00 here, but that's midnight back home."

It wasn't long before they were all in their beds and sleeping soundly.

The next morning, Kai was the first up for the day. She made the coffee, washed the fruit, and got everything set up for breakfast. She was glad to have a few quiet moments by herself, drinking her coffee and sitting on the lanai.

People were beginning to make their way to the pools and bars that separated the resort from Poipu beach. Kai stood and leaned on the railing to get a better view of the water.

"Good morning!" said Lindsay and Michaela as they joined her.

"Good morning!"

For the next few minutes, the three ladies didn't speak. They just took in the sights and sounds that were all around them. Children were laughing, and playing in and around the pool. Teenagers were holding their phones and intently staring at the screens, as if putting them away may cause great harm to the universe. And directly on the ground in front of their lanai were two chickens, quietly pecking the ground to retrieve whatever insects were on the menu for the morning.

"What would you two like to do today after my meeting with Belle?"

Michaela replied, "I wouldn't mind just making this a lazy day around the beach and the pool. I feel like I could use the rest."

"Sounds perfect to me," added Lindsay.

"Then it is unanimous. We'll just hang out here for the day."

Lindsay said, "I can't believe it's been a year since we were here last! It seems that the time just flew by!"

"In some ways it seems the same to me. It's been a very good year," said Kai. "In other ways... not so much," she said, thinking about how much she missed Michael.

Lindsay nodded her head and put her hand on Kai's shoulder. No words were needed.

After breakfast, Kai began to pack towels, snacks, and supplies for their day at the beach. Lindsay and Michaela got changed into their beachwear and met her in the living room.

"Do we have everything?" asked Kai. "Beach towels?"

"Check," said Michaela.

"Sunglasses?"

"Check."

"Sun block?"

"Check."

"Hats?"

"Check."

"Water?"

"Check."

"I think that's everything. Let's get out there."

The beach was in full swing as Kai led her trio to the water's edge. No matter how many times she had seen this beautiful view... it never got old. She never took it for granted. She just took off her sandals, wiggled her toes in the sand and breathed in deeply... holding her breath for a few seconds as if the ambience would somehow fill her spirit even more.

It always did.

Lindsay was already getting settled in to the area they had reserved with three beach chairs, just off of the resort property. Michaela was helping place the items from their beach bag onto each chair.

Kai scanned the beach, finally finding Belle off to her left. She was sitting in the same chairs that Kai had seen so many times before, both in person last year and on her computer screen during their calls.

Belle happened to look up from a book she was reading and saw Kai. She waved and motioned her to come on over.

"Are you ladies ready to go meet Belle?"

"We are," said Michaela.

"I'm a little nervous," said Lindsay.

"Why on earth would you be nervous?" asked Kai.

"Belle is a big deal to me. She's been great for you. She's been on television with that live event you guys watched. It kind of feels like I am about to meet a celebrity."

Kai laughed.

"Belle would be the first to tell you, she is not a celebrity. She doesn't consider herself a big deal at all. She's one of the most kind and humble people I have ever known. The blue hair may seem a bit... eccentric maybe. I guess you might say that she's one of a kind, for sure. But not a celebrity."

"Okay," said Lindsay. "But don't be surprised if I ask for her autograph!"

They all laughed and headed over to Belle's stage on the beach... two azure-colored beach chairs, with a cooler in between, under an umbrella and a palm tree.

By the time they arrived, Belle was already standing and smiling with her arms outstretched.

"Hello! Hello! Hello!"

Kai was the first to get a hug.

"It's so great to see each other in person again!" said Kai. "I can't hug you through the computer!"

"Yes it is! Hugs are so much better here!"

Looking at Michaela, Belle reached out for a hug and said, "How's the brightest eleven-year-old girl in the world doing?"

"I don't know *her*," replied Michaela, laughing. "But I'm doing great!"

"You don't know her?" Belle asked.

"That's my fault. I have her picture here! Hold on!"

Belle reached into her bag and produced a greeting card. It had a picture of Michaela on the front. Belle had saved the picture from one of Kai's social-media posts. She then uploaded it to her service that she used to send out cards to her clients, friends, and family. The caption inside said, "The Brightest Eleven-Year-Old Girl in the World!"

Showing Michaela the greeting card for the first time, Belle said, "Here she is! She's smart! She's kind! She's a great student! And she is stunningly beautiful, just like her mom!"

"My picture on a greeting card? That's so cool! Thank you, Belle!"

"Aww. My pleasure!"

Finally, turning toward Lindsay, Belle reached out and said, "You must be Lindsay! Kai has told me so much about you; it's almost like I already know you. Didn't know you were famous, did you?"

Lindsay looked at Kai and said, "Did you tell her what I said a few seconds ago?"

Kai laughed and shook her head.

"No. That's just Belle!"

"What?" asked Belle with a puzzled look.

Michaela said, "Lindsay was nervous to meet you because she thinks you're a celebrity!"

Lindsay was obviously a little embarrassed.

Belle said, "Oh no, honey. I'm no celebrity. I'm just someone who learned a few things that helped build a good business… and then decided to pass those lessons along to others."

"Rules," Kai said, smiling at Belle.

"That's right. Rules," she replied.

Belle put her hands on Lindsay's shoulders.

"I'll tell you who the true celebrities are, Lindsay. They are people like you. Your friendship with Kai over the years... especially over the last couple of years... has provided such incredible support for her and Michaela. You're one of the reasons they're doing so well. You've had a magnificent impact on the lives of others. In my opinion, that's the best thing any of us can do. I hope you know how truly meaningful that is and how much you are loved."

Lindsay's eyes got teary, even though she was trying very hard not to let that happen.

Belle turned and took Kai's hands.

"And celebrities are people like you, Kai. You experienced such a painful loss at much too early of an age. Still, you picked yourself up and began a new business so that you could take care of this young lady," she said, reaching for Michaela's hand now as well. "The two of you worked to build a great business together. But more importantly, you took care of each other. Even when it hurt and would have been easier to just crawl into bed and cry... you were there for each other."

Now all three were getting teary eyed.

Michaela said, "Well, we did do a little of that crawling-into-bed-and-crying thing too."

They all laughed... through their tears.

"You guys are the true celebrities. As a matter of fact, I want to get each of your autographs right now."

Belle pulled out a bound journal that looked as if she had been keeping it for years. On the front, it simply said, "My Heroes."

She opened the book and flipped through many pages to find the next one that was unmarked.

"Who are all of those people?" asked Michaela. "Are they famous?"

Belle smiled.

"They're famous to me. The world may not know them. But I do. And each of them are heroes of mine for all kinds of different reasons."

She pulled a pen from the bag on her cooler, took a step closer to Michaela and extended both the pen and book to her.

"Will you sign it for me?"

"Cool! I've never given an autograph before!" said Michaela. "Except in our school yearbooks!"

When Michaela had finished, Belle took the pen and the book to Lindsay.

"Lindsay?"

"Of course," said Lindsay, as she accepted the book.

"Thank you for asking me."

"My pleasure. Thank you for signing."

Lindsay handed the book and pen back to Belle.

Turning toward Kai, Belle took a step and stopped. She was struggling to keep her composure.

Belle said softly, "Kai, I am so proud of you. You have amazed me this year. You're definitely one of my heroes. You've accomplished so much and you did so in a way that sets a wonderful example for others." Holding back her own tears now, she said, "Would you do me the honor of signing my book?"

168

Kai couldn't manage to utter a single word. She just looked at her mentor... her friend... and signed.

Looking through the pages, Kai saw a familiar name.

"Is that the Whitney who owns the wedding venue?"

"Yes it is. *Nani Mo'olelo*. She's pretty amazing too, as you know."

Belle looked at everyone and said, "Alright! Enough of that girlie mushy stuff! Let's have some fun!"

That was exactly what the girls needed to put smiles on every face.

Kai said, "Michaela and Lindsay are going over to enjoy the beach for a while as you and I visit."

"That sounds like fun! But you'll be at dinner on Wednesday, right?"

"Yes, ma'am!" said Michaela.

"Wouldn't miss it," added Lindsay.

As Michaela and Lindsay departed, Kai and Belle took their seats on their chairs in the sand.

"So what's going on in your world? Is there anything specific you'd like to discuss?" asked Belle.

"Not really," replied Kai. "I just wanted to visit with you... and thank you for all you've done for me."

"My pleasure. We can certainly do that. We can talk about anything. It doesn't have to be about business."

Kai thought for a minute.

"Well, maybe there is one thing I'd like to get your thoughts on."

"What's that?"

Kai continued. "I've made a friend over the last several months... a man friend."

Belle's interest was piqued.

"Hmm? Go on."

"His name is Dalton. He's been pretty helpful when I needed things."

Belle got a curious smile on her face, raised an eyebrow and asked, "What do you mean? Define *helpful when you needed things*?"

Kai laughed. "Not that, Belle! Just helpful! When things would break around the house, he would help me learn how to fix them."

"So, he didn't repair them? Instead, he helped you learn how to do it yourself?"

"Yes."

Belle said, "I like this guy!"

Kai laughed. "I do too. But he wants to take the friendship a little further. I'm not sure that I'm ready for that right now. Michaela and I are perfectly fine. She's happy. She's doing well in school. Our business is doing well. I don't know that I want to bring anything into that mix that might upset the balance we have. At least not yet."

"So, how do you know he wants to take things a little further?"

Kai replied, "Funny story. Just before Halloween, I overheard him talking with Michaela. He wanted to know how she might feel about the idea of him asking me out on a date. He seemed to really care about her feelings. I actually thought it was quite sweet. Michaela, being her usual funny self said, 'Don't you think you should be asking my mom for *her* opinion rather than me?'"

"And?" asked Belle.

"And he's asked me out for dinner and a movie a couple of times since. Both times I already had plans for the evening. I assured him that I wasn't just blowing him off. But at the same time, I was kind of glad I could push the idea a little into the future."

Kai looked at Belle. "What do you think?"

Belle thought about her answer.

"I don't know that I'm the best person to ask for dating advice. That being said, I think that you pushed the decision back because it feels uncomfortable to you. If that's the case, allow yourself those feelings without worry. You don't have to do anything. But it's also perfectly okay for you to be ready if and when the time comes that it feels right. My opinion is that whatever is right for you and Michaela is the right answer. And from what you said about... what's his name?"

"Dalton."

"Yes. Dalton. From what you said about Dalton, I think he'll be okay with any answer you give."

"Oh, I think so too. But I'm a little worried that I may wait, then finally decide that I would like the same thing, only for him to have already found someone else. He's such a nice person. He's handsome. He seems to be really in touch with how people around him feel about things."

"Sounds like quite a catch."

"He is," replied Kai. "I'm just not sure that I want to go fishing yet."

Belle laughed.

"Then do my version of environmentally friendly dating... strictly catch and release!"

Kai laughed.

Belle said, "Kai, you said something there that I would encourage you to think about a little differently."

"What?"

"Being worried that he may find someone else before you are ready."

Belle said, "First things first. Let go of the worry. It's wasted emotional energy. I know that's easier said than done. But do your best. And second, timing is probably not all that important. I tend to think if it's supposed to happen, it will. If it's not, then it is best that it doesn't. If it turns out that he becomes 'the one that got away,' and if you still want a relationship, throw your line in again."

Belle continued. "Seriously. Think about this. You are a strong and beautiful woman who's rebuilt a great life for you and your daughter. You don't really need a man in your life in order for you to be okay. That's the way it should be. You don't need a knight to ride in on a white horse and save the day. You have ridden in on your own white horse and the day is doing quite well."

Kai smiled.

"At the same time, if you decide that you do want a man in your life again, let it happen organically. Don't rush into a decision based on the fear that someone may not be available later. That can cause you to make some long-term mistakes. Just remember that you are in a position of peace and confidence now. You've built a life that works for you. Should you decide that you want to have a relationship, the ideal candidate would be someone who has also built a life that works well for them as well. Then you two can be supportive of each other as you enjoy the overlapping part of your time that becomes your new relationship."

"If that's what you want, look for someone who will love you in such a way that it makes you both better people."

Kai nodded.

Belle leaned forward as if sharing a secret and quietly asked, "But most importantly… how does he look in jeans?"

"Belle!" Kai exclaimed.

"What? You guys live in Texas! I've seen those cowboys in their jeans!" she said as she fanned her face with her hand. "Whoo!"

The two ladies laughed.

When the laughter had subsided, they were both silent for a couple of minutes.

Then Kai said, "By the way…"

Belle raised her eyebrows.

"He looks really great in those jeans."

They laughed again.

Belle and Kai spent the rest of their hour just talking about the world and enjoying their day.

Kai, Michaela, and Lindsay spent Monday afternoon, all day on Tuesday, and Wednesday morning enjoying the beauty that is so prevalent in Hawaii. They snorkeled Nualolo Kai reef. They took a helicopter tour of Mt. Waialeale, the Na Pali Coast, Manawaiopuna Falls, and Waimea Canyon State Park. And they enjoyed a luau at the Smith Family Garden.

As Wednesday evening rolled around, they were all very excited to go to Belle's home for dinner.

"Welcome!" said Belle as she answered the door. "Please, come in!"

Belle's house was a gorgeous two-bedroom cottage with a lanai that framed an unobstructed view of the ocean. The home decor was beautifully interesting, like Belle herself. The living room was filled with an imaginative combination of furniture styles and colors, floral arrangements, and artwork.

"I love your home, Belle!" said Kai.

"Thank you!"

Lindsay walked to the open doors that led out to the lanai and said, "This view is amazing!"

Belle replied, "I'd have to agree. I looked for quite a while before choosing this place. It has been a great joy to live here."

"Would you ladies like a glass of wine before dinner?"

"I know I would!" replied Michaela.

"Nice try, young lady," Belle said with a smile. "I made you a special juice for the evening. It has pineapple, coconut, orange juice, and vanilla. I also put a little strawberry on top to make it pretty."

"That sounds way better than wine!" Michaela said with a smile.

Belle retrieved two bottles of wine. One was a Pinot Noir from her wine rack. The second was a Chardonnay from her wine cooler.

As Belle opened the wines, Kai saw the label, which she immediately recognized.

"Wow! Those are wines from Special Memories!"

"It seemed appropriate for the evening," replied Belle with a smile.

Kai asked, "Where did you get them? I could've sent you some."

Belle laughed and replied, "That's okay. They were actually given to me by a new business friend of mine."

"Well that is a very good friend. Those are two of the best that we have available."

After everyone's glass was filled, Belle raised her glass for a toast.

"Here's to great friends, fine wine, and special memories!"

Glasses clinked as the ladies smiled.

"That would make a great advertising slogan for us" said Kai.

After taking their first sips, Belle said, "I have a little bit of an announcement to make."

"What is it?" asked Kai.

Belle smiled.

"I just bought a new company a couple of weeks ago. There haven't been any announcements yet, but I am really excited."

"That's great, Belle! What kind of company? What's the name?" asked Lindsay.

Belle didn't answer immediately. Instead, she walked to the table, picked up one of the bottles of wine, and turned back to her guests.

Holding up the bottle, she smiled and said, "This one."

"What?"

"That's awesome!"

"This is incredible!"

Everyone was excited about the news.

Belle said, "And Kai, that is our new advertising slogan."

"I love it! I was about to ask, why didn't you tell me before?" said Kai. "But I think making the announcement this way was so much better!"

"It did have a certain amount of flare to it, didn't it?" replied Belle.

"Yes it did! I am so excited! Congratulations!"

"Thank you!"

"As a matter of fact, that's why I bought the new car. It was a little reward for myself."

Lindsay said, "That's a nice little reward! That car is gorgeous!"

"Thank you, Lindsay!"

"What do you think about it, Kai? Do you like it?"

"I do, indeed!"

"That's fortunate." Belle said.

Puzzled, Kai asked, "Why do you say that?"

Belle explained, "One of the first programs that I'm adding to Special Memories Wine Club is a car-bonus program. Based on their sales volume, qualifiers will win a one-year lease on various cars. Then they can requalify each year by hitting that year's target. The one you're driving this week is for the top-level qualifiers."

"I like that idea!" exclaimed Kai.

"I'm glad to hear you say that. I decided to go ahead and implement the program retroactively for this year's sales team."

Kai began to see where this was going. "And?"

Belle smiled and said, "You qualified, Kai! When you get back to the airport, you won't need anyone to pick you up. I'm having yours delivered there. It will be waiting for you."

"Oh my gosh! You're kidding, right?"

"Of course not, silly. That would be mean!"

Kai hugged Belle.

"Thank you so much! I don't know what to say."

"Say you'll keep qualifying! That's what!"

Everyone laughed.

What was planned as a dinner, turned into an unexpected celebration. It was a very special evening indeed.

With the exception of her wedding to Michael and the birth of Michaela, Kai couldn't remember a more special week. Nothing was anticipated. Everything was so meaningful. But now, unfortunately, it was Sunday morning and time to return home.

Kai, Michaela, and Lindsay drove to Belle's home first, so that she could bring her car back from the airport. Belle got into the driver's seat and said, "Let's see how this baby drives."

"You'll love it!" said Kai.

"I already do!" said the lady with the blue hair.

The drive to the airport only took about thirty minutes or so. The ladies enjoyed the conversation and the company… but they all realized that the sadness of saying goodbye was just a page turn away.

As they pulled into the passenger drop-off section and removed the luggage from the trunk, Michaela ran up to Belle and hugged her tightly.

"I'm going to miss you, Belle! This has been the best week ever!"

"What do you mean, you're going to miss me? Your mom and I will still be having our calls. You'll see me anytime you want. We may even see each other more, now that I bought the company."

Michaela nodded her head.

"It's been so nice to meet you, Belle." Lindsay said, also giving her a hug. "Kai is right. You're pretty amazing."

"Thank you, sweetie."

Kai looked at Belle through eyes that had begun to fill with tears.

"I'm such a sap! I guess I got that from Michael. I know that I'll see you Friday on my laptop. But I like this in person thing much better. Thank you for everything, Belle. I have never had anyone…" Kai struggled to speak. "I don't know how I could ever repay your kindness. But thank you."

Belle gave Kai a hug and said, "That answer is easy. You don't need to repay that kindness to me. Instead, pick someone else and repay my kindness to them. You're ready to be a mentor now. And I can't think of a better way to honor our relationship than you becoming that mentor for another."

"I will. I would be honored to keep it going."

Kai smiled sheepishly at Belle. "Would I need to color my hair blue?"

"Only if you really want to" replied Belle, laughing.

Michaela spoke up and said, "Gee Mom! I wonder if Dalton likes blue?"

Kai shushed Michaela as everyone laughed.

Goodbyes were said. Tears began to subside. And soon, everyone was in their seats and preparing for takeoff.

Kai recognized the face of the flight attendant in first class.

"I think you were on our flight home last year," said Kai.

The lady smiled and said, "I'm sorry. I don't really remember."

"You mean I'm not the only passenger you've met in the last twelve months?" asked Kai sarcastically but with a smile. "No apology necessary."

"I'm Kai Frazier," she said, extending her hand.

"Hi, Kai. I'm Wendy. Nice to meet you."

"If I remember correctly, you live in McKinney, right?"

"Wow! Good memory!"

Kai laughed, "Well, you may have met hundreds of passengers over the last twelve months. But I have only met four flight attendants during that time... and you're two of them!"

The two ladies laughed.

"Were you here on business or pleasure?"

"Both, actually. Our family has taken a trip to Kauai each December for the last several years. But this year, I was also spending time with a very dear mentor and friend."

"That sounds fun!" said Wendy. "I'm glad that you remembered me, but this may be the last time you see me in this role."

"Why is that?"

She smiled and said, "I've just gotten my real-estate license and I'll be selling homes soon."

"I'm sure you'll be great at that! You seem great with people."

"Thanks. I wish I had the same confidence as you do. This will be my first sales position, and that scares me a little."

"Been there. Done that. In wine sales instead of real-estate. But I remember that feeling well."

Wendy continued, "My husband and I got a divorce a few months back. He is still very involved in our son's life and certainly meets his financial responsibilities. But I've decided that I need to develop a new career where I can earn more money than I make as a flight attendant."

"I'm sorry about your divorce. That's got to be hard. I lost my husband about a year and a half ago."

"I'm sorry," replied Wendy.

Kai thought for a couple of moments, remembering Belle's parting words.

"Wendy. I've experienced a lot of the things that you'll be going through, and if you'll allow me to, I'd like to help."

Kai thought about her next sentence and it made her smile. "I'm part of a group of women who have decided to mentor other women in business and life. Would you want to exchange contact information?"

Wendy wasn't sure why, but she trusted Kai. That hadn't been her pattern for a couple of years now. Trusting didn't come easy for her anymore. Still, she agreed and said yes.

The two ladies swapped phone numbers and email addresses.

Wendy smiled and went about her duties attending to the passengers.

Kai drifted off to sleep.

7 Rules for Success in Direct Sales Said the Lady with the Blue Hair

Rule Number One: *The Stewardess Rule* — Secure your own oxygen mask before attempting to assist others.

Build your business or career first. Then you will be able to help others do the same and support the charities you deem the most important.

Rule Number Two: *The Success Rule* — You can be successful at anything in life as long as enough people know what you do.

First, find a product or service that you truly believe in. Make it something that you wholeheartedly feel makes someone's life better when they own it. Something that would even give you a greater sense of self-worth by the simple fact that you helped them find it.

Then do what it takes to let enough people know and understand how you can help make their lives better with your product or service.

Rule Number Three: *The Consistency Rule* — You can't control a lot of things. But you *can* control how consistent you are.

You can't control whether people say "yes" or "no" to buying from you. But you *can* be consistent in asking if they would like to buy. You can't control how many others will want to join your team. But you *can* be consistent in making the opportunity available to them. You can't control the various things that life will often send your way.

183

But you *can* be consistent in how you respond with a great attitude, a careful plan, and an expectancy that you can find good things from most situations. Even tough situations can teach valuable lessons.

Rule Number Four: *The Wood Stove Rule* — You have to put wood in the stove first before it will ever provide heat for you.

Don't stand in front of a wood stove and say, "Give me heat first. Then I will give you wood." You have to invest in the wood first in order to receive the heat. Treat your business like a wood stove. Be willing to feed it first—and then it will provide for you. You will need to invest in your business.

Rule Number Five: *The Miniskirt Rule* — Think of your presentations like your miniskirt.

Keep them short enough to hold people's attention but long enough to cover the goods.

Rule Number Six: *The Rising Tide Rule* — A rising tide lifts all boats. Be that tide.

Be willing to share your knowledge and experience with others. It's easy to share with members of your team. Their success will directly impact your income. Also be willing to share with those whose success will have no bearing on your business. Give from your heart and your wisdom with the sincere desire that something you say truly makes someone else's life better.

Exception to the rule: Refrain from giving unwanted advice to friends and family about how they should live their lives, unless you first ask for permission, otherwise you may need to wear protective clothing.

Rule Number Seven: *The Naughty Rule* — If you aren't getting in trouble once in a while, you simply aren't trying hard enough.

Remember that innovation happens when gifted people follow their vision. Don't let, 'Because that's the way we've always done it' become your mantra. What would you do if you knew that you couldn't fail? Great things often happen because someone was creative and brave enough to try.

Pay attention to wise counsel from your mentors. Then experiment. Try new methods. Stretch your mind and do things that get you out of your comfort zone. If that occasionally gets you into a little hot water — add some bubble bath, grab a glass of champagne, close your eyes, and relax.

About the Authors

LISA M. WILBER was named Avon's "Woman of Enterprise", the top honor given to independent representatives by the company. She has also been included numerous times on "The 50 Most Influential People in Direct Sales" list and earned Avon's "Yellow Rose of Courage". Other awards include being named the "Top Female Network Marketer in the  World" and voted the "Ambitious Women's Choice Award".

Lisa has been selling and team building for Avon since 1981 when she was 18 years old. When Avon introduced their network marketing program entitled "Leadership", Lisa was able to attain the top level of achievement within 15 months of joining the program. She and her team have consistently performed in the top 10 in team sales volume in the United States for over 25 years. Attaining her professional status with the National Speaker's Association, she has conducted seminars around the world including Canada, Ireland, the UK and across the United States. Lisa Wilber is the author of three books and the co-author of half a dozen more, including her trademark anthology book series entitled "A View from the Top" which includes chapters by over 60 top leaders in Avon.

Connect with Lisa on social media: https://www.facebook.com/lisa.wilber

JEFF C. WEST is the award winning author of the heartwarming sales fable, *The Unexpected Tour Guide*, winner of the Axiom Business Books Bronze Award in the Business Fable Category. He has been a guest on numerous national and international sales and leadership programs such as *The Go-Giver Podcast with Bob Burg, The Go-Giver*

Community's Conversations With Legends, The Buyer's Mind with Jeff Shore, The Author Your Brand Show with Doug Crowe, The Business Growth Advantage with Joey C. Vitale and many more.

With over thirty years of successful sales and sales leadership experience, including 21 years with the *Fortune 500®* insurance company, Aflac, Jeff is a sought-after speaker in multiple industries and his client list includes companies such as Aflac, Edward Jones, Link Staffing and others.